music of the spheres

Books by Guy Murchie

Men on the Horizon
Song of the Sky
Music of the Spheres

music of the spheres

*The Material Universe—From Atom
to Quasar, Simply Explained*

By

guy murchie

With illustrations by the author

IN TWO VOLUMES

VOL. I. THE MACROCOSM:

Planets, Stars, Galaxies, Cosmology

DOVER PUBLICATIONS, INC., NEW YORK

Published in Canada by General Publishing Company, Ltd., 30 Lesmill Road, Don Mills, Toronto, Ontario.

This Dover edition, first published in 1967, is a revised version of the work originally published in a one-volume clothbound edition in 1961. This Dover edition is published by special arrangement with Houghton Mifflin Company, publisher of the original edition.

Library of Congress Catalog Card Number: 67-22255

Manufactured in the United States of America
Dover Publications, Inc.
180 Varick Street
New York, N.Y. 10014

TO MY BROTHER

DONALD

who loved the waves and
the spangled sky

There is geometry in the humming
of the strings. There is music in the
spacings of the spheres.

PYTHAGORAS
5th century B.C.

fOREWORD to the DOVER EDITION

THIS book was originally published by Houghton Mifflin Company in 1961 as a single hard-cover volume, and by 1966 had had five printings, including a special one of over 30,000 copies for the Christian Herald Bookshelf. But continuing demand for a current and widely available version has led to the present low-priced Dover edition of 1967 which has been brought up to date with new material relating to the major developments in astronomy and physics since 1961, particularly the findings of the historic rocket probes of Venus and Mars by Mariners II and IV in 1962 and 1965, the dramatic discovery of quasars in 1963, and the proliferation of subatomic particles from thirty to more than a hundred in half a decade.

In the meantime I am six years along in writing a sequel and companion volume to *Music of the Spheres* on the subjects of life and mind. The work, now about half done, will probably be titled *Melody of Life,* and in due time I hope it will be offered with the present book as an integral set.

Marlborough, N.H.   **G.M.**
1967

acknowledgments

Duration the six years of full-time study and labor I have put into this book, I have had assistance and inspiration from hundreds of sources — most constantly of all from my wife Käthe, who distracts me from distractions while working as best she can to keep the grass greener on our side of the fence. And among many others no one has helped me more than Professor Mael A. Melvin, now in Argentina, who gave me a brainstirring, concentrated course in atomic physics, and Per Lowdin, professor of chemistry in Uppsala, Sweden, who cleared up many a cloudy paradox with his beautiful articulation.

Likewise I have been assisted by Astronomy Professor Samuel Herrick of the University of California (who answered questions about space and stars), by Professor Harlow Shapley (who looked over my astronomical illustrations and discussed the universe) and other astronomers of Harvard Observatory (who read or criticized various chapters on moons, planets and stars), by astronomer Seth B. Nicholson (who was hospitable to my proposed names for the eight nameless moons of Jupiter, four of which he himself discovered), by Professor Aage Bohr of the Copenhagen Institute for Theoretical Physics, by Professor Gerald Holton (who helped my chapter on relativity without approving of it) and other physicists, mathematicians and philosophers at Harvard and Massachusetts Institute of Technology, by Giorgio de Santillana, professor of the history of science at M.I.T. (who read the whole manuscript with a constructive eye), by Michael Powsner, a rare and generous science teacher of South Shaftsbury, Vermont (who gave books, time and ideas), by Daniel Comstock, an engineer with imagination (who gave me my first lesson in relativity), by Mervin J. Kelly, president emeritus of Bell Telephone Laboratories, by Willy Ley, authority on space travel, by R. Buckminster Fuller the geometric philosopher, by Isaac Asimov the science writer (who criticized the manuscript in detail), by Gerald Brenan the historian of Spain, who told me the story of ancient Sybaris (pages 363–365), by Martin Gardner whose writings in *Scientific American* were an important source for the discussion of reflections, handedness and symmetry on pages 432 and 482–485, by H. A. Rey on whose ingeniously graphic drawings of the constellations are based the illustrations on pages 167, 168 and 178, and by several highly competent editors, particularly Betsy Pitha who made many constructive suggestions while gently working her fine-toothed comb through both the text and illustrations.

Of course none of these generous persons can be held responsible for the errors that must still be lurking somewhere in these pages. The authorship of all surviving boners, alas, must remain mine alone.

Among periodicals my most consistently valuable source has been *Scientific American*, with occasionally useful gleanings also from *American Scientist, Main Currents, Navigation, The New York Times* and the science section of *Time*. And the following books have contributed significantly: *A History of Science* by George Sarton, *Introduction to Astronomy* by Cecilia Payne-Gaposchkin, *Earth, Moon and Planets* by Fred L. Whipple, *The Stars* by H. A. Rey, *Frontiers of Astronomy* by Fred Hoyle, *Concerning the Nature of Things* by Sir William Bragg, *The Physical Basis of Things* by John A. Eldridge, *General Chemistry* by Linus Pauling, *Matter, Earth and Sky* by George Gamow, *The Strange Story of the Quantum* by Banesh Hoffmann, *Light and Colour in the Open Air* by M. Minnaert, *The Analysis of Matter* by Bertrand Russell, *Space, Time and Gravitation* by Sir Arthur Eddington, *The Principle of Relativity* by Albert Einstein, H. A. Lorentz, H. Weyl and H. Minkowski, *Physics and Philosophy* by Werner Heisenberg, *Philosophy of Science* by Philipp Frank, and many others, the more important of which are mentioned by name in the text.

G. M.

1961

contents to part one

moons of rock and suns of fire

moons of rock and suns of fire

1. out from the breathing earth

THE STARS BENEATH MY FEET stare upward, strange and bold. They do not twinkle. They burn steadfastly in the black, bottomless sky.

My watch says 02:40 Universal Time. But it is not really night. That searchlight glaring at us is the sun. That toenail of crescent beside it the new moon, bright as snow, even its dark side illumined so clearly I can recognize Mare Imbrium without using the telescope.

Most conspicuous of all is the great pale-blue ball that fills a third of the void: the earth, by far the most positive thing outside our ship within reach of my senses — a matriarch of gravity leaning out at us from ink-black space — a somethingness rolling through nothingness. Its dappled surface, here crisp and clear-grained, there soft and filmy, is pure blue between the curved storms and lesser suds of white cloud areas, while on one side a fiery highlight of sunshine reflects off the glassy Pacific Ocean.

If I must admit to feeling a little giddy right now perhaps it is just the break-off, sometimes called "space dumps," that the satellite pioneers used to complain of — a sort of apprehensive loneliness that no amount of friendly banter with the rest of my crew seems really able to shake. With conscious casualness I stoop to wipe the floor port with my magnetic rag and gasp again at my incapacity to comprehend those stars below as well as above me. Or are they really not below me but just over there and out here or this way and that way?

Although I have read about space all my life, nothing I've learned could begin to prepare me for the reality. The utter and soul-draining blackness of that gulf that drops away and down and down to infinity! I am as a mosquito lost at night over the Pacific Ocean. And the real Pacific that was once so endless — I can see it still down there as but the shining cheek of a world that has fallen from my feet. My aloneness is breath-taking.

But I think I am already getting used to the relaxation, the weightlessness of space — it is like swimming, only more so — though the lack of a definite up or down will take longer. Not that that alarms my mind, which can consciously adjust, but it does provoke a hollow corporal insecurity somewhere beyond the reach of the will.

Time will soon reply to these questions, of course, especially if time up here in space is part of time on Earth. So far it seems to be — but one should not be hasty in such matters. Time changes with speed, and every vortex of gravity may have its own. Besides, I am trespassing on the future here. I mean that I am really *not* here yet in the common terrestrial understanding for, at the present writing, men have not quite attained to permanent habitable stations in space — although as surely as winter is followed by spring they will have done so shortly after this book is published.

Nonetheless, for all my inability to be here in flesh at the earthly moment I am still inevitably here in the truer larger sense — in future body almost as surely as in present mind. For robot space stations are already fixtures of our local sky and better ones abuilding on Earth and who knows in how many other places in both ancient and future days? Thus my presence in this borrowed space is a symbolic certainty and a true part of the very time-space continuum I am venturing to explore.

I say "venturing" advisedly, for if you don't think this passage through the boundless unknown is a venture I humbly wish you would just try it yourself sometime — whether or not you have a body fit to accompany you as, we shall presently see, may not much longer be so very important.

"Why?" you may ask. "Why should I stir from my accustomed ways for the risks and trials of space? What could be my motive? Have I not trouble enough already on the earth I was made for?"

Yes, you have trouble on Earth all right, I admit. But who told you you were made for Earth trouble alone? Space is part of the world — your world if you have the stuff to make it yours. Did anyone warn the birds that the air was only for bees and bugs? Do you suppose God put the stars here just to look at? Did He draw a boundary to your piece of sky?

I say space and time are as inevitably yours as the wind and the sea and you cannot refuse them. Man must respond to his destiny. He has already knocked on the upper door and it is opening. The hinges will not be stayed.

As if this were not reason enough to be here riding an intangible orbit with faith in Newton for my fuel, I have a world of other reasons. The earth has been rolling blindly through the void for some five billion years, slowly developing an organ of consciousness, and it is just now arriving at the stage where it is capable of seeing and understanding itself. Its stones and rivers have begun to speak and its winds at last have found their tongues in the mind of man. The very layers of the soil, the grain of glaciers, the rings of trees, even the sea bottoms have become living pages of our world's diary that she may read back to herself for the first time.

Thus you and I have been appointed to a greater consciousness than our own. Man has become the Self of the material earth — in a larger symbolic sense, perhaps potentially a cell of the consciousness of the whole time-space universe. So I say it behooves him to enlarge his view, to accept life's new dimension when it is offered — to adopt the perspective of space.

Indeed, there is a greater nature up here, a nature that does not abhor a vacuum or trust a parallel line. Space is where heat no longer rises, where things fall not down but along, where gravity can push as well as pull, and even the straightest lines are curves. It is where you begin to happen to events instead of just letting events happen to you. It is where you must be on constant guard against the dangers of "common sense." It is where scientists and philosophers will be finding not only deeper answers to their questions but deeper questions for their answers. It is the home of unworldly dreams and undreamed-of worlds, of globes of fire and clouds of spinning gas, of emptiness impenetrable, of planets inhabitable, of moons incredible. It is the major reality of the material world, the first vantage place for outer knowledge. I have come here with open eyes to see the unseen. I have come with open mind to listen for the music of the spheres.

To understand what this fantastic world is all about — to see its basic pattern and meaning — I must crane my soul to examine it deeply and, in so far as is possible, independently. I must seek a perspective far beyond the traditional, beyond the safe and proper, even beyond the human. I must see not only out of my own eyes here and now but out of lenses and soul-ports on the undiscovered planet Umkrid 22 in the dry spring of the year 47,909! It is an ambitious aim for a book of twentieth-century earthly publication.

Since one must begin somewhere, let me begin with the most familiar, our home sphere, then branch outward to the moon and sun and stars. Then inward to the dazzling cosmos of the atom — to space, to time and their relations — deferring until later a close look at life, at the mind and the spirit — yet essaying, if it be permitted me, a humble muse upon the meaning of it all.

One of the first things to be noted about our home sphere, the earth, is that it is not a sphere. Instead, although the eye alone cannot detect it, it is more exactly what a geometrician would call an oblate spheroid with a faint tendency toward the pear shape, a sort of fat doorknob gently flattened at the spindle poles, worn from long handling in some places but in need of sandpapering in others — perhaps a little on the warped side or, if you'll pardon my saying so, slightly skewed. In fact, one could never define its shape precisely, for it is not only hopelessly irregular in detail but constantly changing. In a very real sense it is alive. Like an animal it stirs in its sleep, it "breathes" air, it grows, its wounds heal, its juices circulate, its skin metabolizes, its nerves crackle quietly with vital messages. It even rumbles with internal gas and dreams and itches a little and (through its inhabitants) feels self-conscious.

This living aspect of the earth is something you don't hear much about in geography classes, but it is hard to miss from my new space-eye view. Beside the obvious rhythms of the swirling waves of weather folding over and over each other, the steady advance of the soft twilight edge of night and the ever-changing atmospheric colors, the solid flesh of Earth itself where visible seems to blush and glow with the hours. The great western plains of wheat reflect light differently after a wide shift of wind. The green of shallow seas deepens toward blue with the rise of tides. The Gulf Stream and the jet stream change courses in the heat of an afternoon. Looking at large mountain chains, one can even sense the slow lateral movement of continents steadily pinching the loose skin of the planet.

Of course, geophysicists know that this life rhythm of the globe does not stop at the surface but continues right through its middle, that not only the sea and the air have regular tides but the very rock gently nods to the beck of the moon, and waves tuned to the sun literally pierce the planet's heart. A single stone or a granite cliff naturally seems too brittle in human eyes to have any springiness in it, yet a crystallized rocky crust the size of the earth proves to be more flexible than steel and molds itself almost perfectly to the flows of the material below, which is increasingly fluent with depth. The black basalt yields to what is deduced to be pliable greenish olivine in the first fifty miles; within a few hundred more this becomes a plastic mantle of silica or magnesia or perhaps iron oxide, turning completely liquid halfway to the center (as is proved by seismic waves); and there is almost surely some sort of alloy of molten nickel-iron at the core.

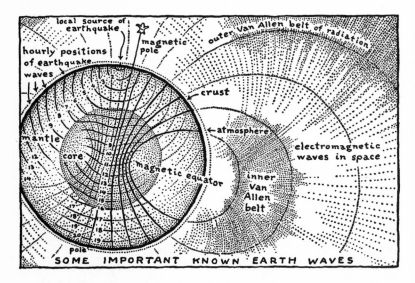

Although the pressures are so great in the earth's depths (up to four million times the greatest atmospheric pressure) that even "liquids" may be twice as "solid" as steel, there is definitely some free flow of substance. Indeed, shock waves that reach the surface as earthquakes and mysterious slow tides involving magnetism and gravity and modulating the actual shape of the planet continue to pulse through it like bile and adrenalin in the body.

The earth's magnetism, for example, evidently has a strong primary field geared to its axis of rotation with various overlapping lesser components that shift continuously. These residual magnetic fields recently were measured to move irregularly westward at an average rate of more than a mile a month, completing a full revolution about every 1,600 years — thus suggesting that the earth's moving core and mantle exert a force upon each other comparable to the armature and field coils of an electric motor. The poles of the earth, both geographic and magnetic, have likewise been deduced to shift, in this case only a few inches a year. The calculation goes back to the year 700,000,-000 B.C., when the North Pole seems to have been in what is now Arizona, then probably a swamp or a shallow area of the great world sea.

The flowings of earthly materials of different densities also create cryptic patterns of subnormal and supernormal gravity on the surface, like the recently discovered sinuous band of low gravity in the East Indies, where everything weighs a little less and a champion javelin thrower has an advantage of nearly a foot over some of his rivals in higher latitudes.

A beginning of conception of the temperature increase with depth into the earth can be had by visiting the "world's deepest well," an old borehole of the Continental Oil Company near Wasco, California, where you can cook your coffee just by lowering it 15,000 feet or less. For rocks reach the boiling point of water in the first two or three miles below the solid surface practically everywhere on Earth, and there is an increase of something like 50° F. with every mile of descent from then on (assuming pressure is the determining factor and not mainly the radioactivity of the earth's skin as some think). The rate gradually diminishes until the temperature levels off, according to present estimates, somewhere around 6,700° F. at the center.

The long-range effect of this cauldron of moiling, boiling rock and metal of course has been to brew a surface slag of earth just such as we know today, but which has by no means yet finished cooking. In fact, if the phases it has already gone through are any indication, it will look and be startlingly different in a mere hundred thousand years and in a few million you will scarcely know it as the same world. The present mountains, for example, are just a momentary frown on the earth's face — passing wrinkles that have only at long intervals appeared before and will never be the same again. During almost all of her five billion years of life the earth's face has been much smoother than we can remember it, the oceans shallower, the continents lower, smaller and swampier. In fact, much of the time since the oceans first appeared they have covered the earth so evenly that there were scarcely more than a few strange-shaped islands (such as the primordial Labrador) in the single world ocean and much less contrast of climate between the equator and the poles, the seasons unnoticeable, and most winds tradewinds that blew all through the shorter days and nights and years and under the heavier clouds that seldom parted to let the fish and crabs and insects see the bigger, faster moon.

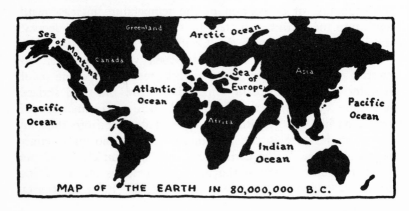

MAP OF THE EARTH IN 80,000,000 B.C.

It has only been now and then during relatively brief periods of shrinkage that the earth's crisp skin has had to wrinkle much to fit the cooling, contracting mantle beneath it. Between times the mantle may well expand, splitting the surface along seams known as rifts, while the wrinkles are quickly worn down to gentle plains by the constant grindstones of rain and wind and sand that have been measured to erode away all exposed parts of the land at the average rate of about an inch a century. Naturally this wear is hundreds of times faster on mountain crags or in the beds of rushing streams, but in settled valleys (as in the oceans) there occurs the reverse of erosion, a piling up of sediment and vegetable and animal matter and debris of civilization, preserving history for the archaeologists. Also, the average erosion pace is naturally slowed down in the gentler ages when there are no mountains. But still there has to be an over-all net erosion gain on land else the mountains would get out of hand, and all geological evidence shows that the intermittent swelling and crinkling of the mantle — which has altered the earth's circumference by amounts probably as great as 100 miles since the oceans formed — has been more than matched by the smoothing out of wrinkles faster than they came. In fact, nearly two miles' depth of solid granite has been washed and blown off the land's entire face, counting pinnacle and plain alike, just during the oceanic ages. This is shown by the fact that the salt now dissolved in all the oceans, if spread out uniformly over the land, would make a layer 450 feet thick — 450 feet being 5 percent of "nearly two miles" — while practically all of the salt has been traced to granite rock of which it also forms 5 percent.

Naturally, it is an effort of imagination to visualize this crimping and grinding, this rhythmic roughening and polishing of the earth. But the evidence of it is not out of reach. I need little more than to shift to a coarser time-gear in my sense of perspective to see the fleeting flesh in what poets used to call the "everlasting hills," the surgery of rivers, the chewing of rock by invisible jaws of air, the rasping hoofs of glaciers, even the now-rough, now-gentle uplifting of whole continents. Consider the placid Buena Vista oil field in California, which looks like the epitome of *terra firma* but which geologists find is rising steadily half an inch a year, four feet a century. This dull rate ceases to be dull the instant you multiply the centuries ahead to notice that, if it holds its pace, Buena Vista will be two miles taller than the present Mount Everest (likewise rising) before even a million more years have fled. And of course, a million-year-old mountain is just a shoulder-shrug to an earth that already counts her years in the billions.

Like matter itself, *terra firma* thus reveals her illusory nature. Every peaceful cornfield becomes a potential Paricutin of smoke and brimstone, every little fissure a San Andreas Fault of threatening earthquake catastrophe. Of such are mountains born and raised — too slowly for mortal eye to see — too slowly to be noticed by the full sweep of human history — yet literally bursting and buckling and boiling in the view of the patient moon, who has reason enough to know the meaning of violence as anyone can see in her pitted face.

If creation of mountains needs a long view for appreciation, the building of continents needs a still longer one. Yet both are essentially the same process on scales of differing magnitude. All the earth's crust, including the seas, is floating on the molten basalt and olivine some ten to fifty miles down and, like icebergs in water, all parts of the solid crust displace volumes of the sub-liquid exactly in proportion to their weight. Thus the continents, being made of relatively more of the lighter granite,

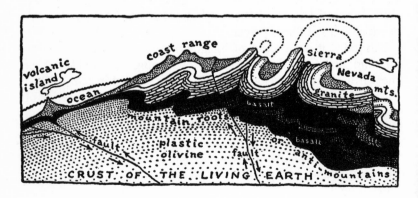

float higher than the denser basalt ocean floors, and every mountain must balance its height with a similar depth reaching unseen far into the dark fluid beneath. This is so literally true,
say geologists, that removing mountains will have the same kind
of difficulty for future atomic engineers that eliminating old wil-
lows had for our forebears: no sooner will they get the mountain
leveled clean than the lightened "stump" will start to rise
again, floating on olivine, and this resprouting will likely continue in diminishing degree until the last stubborn root has
been painstakingly dug away.

What is true of rock applies in less degree also to rock's shifty
burden of ice in the form of glaciers crawling on the floating
rock and of pack ice drifting on the sea that rests on floating
rock. Looking over the earth carefully, I notice that a full tenth
of all its land is covered with glacial ice, mostly in Antarctica
and Greenland, with a slight sprinkling in the warmer zones.
And if I thumb back through the pages of geologic time, it is
apparent that these glaciers are the remains of the last ice age,
which covered about a third of the land some twenty thousand
years ago. The ice age was the fourth in the current series of ice
ages which, according to the most plausible present theory, was
caused primarily by the aforementioned wandering of the earth's
axis of rotation, which only a few million years ago brought
the North Pole from the Pacific to the Arctic Ocean. Although
the cooling effect of oblique and reduced sunlight in the polar
zone had previously been offset by the relatively free circulation
of the vast Pacific waters, this source of warmth was left behind
as the axis swung farther into the Arctic confines. And after the
water evaporating from the cooling Arctic Ocean had produced
so much snow and therefore such a volume of glaciation that
the earth's sea level ebbed nearly three hundred feet (exposing
much of the undersea ridge that joins Iceland to the British

Isles), the Arctic became so dammed up and isolated that it froze over. By this time, however, the ice age had reached a maximum. The crust over the Arctic Ocean cut off evaporation, humidity and snowfall so drastically that the glaciers were reduced to a slower growing rate in winter than their melting rate in summer with the result that they gradually dwindled down toward nothing. This net melting in turn raised the sea level again, restoring circulation and warmth to the Arctic until it was once more an open sea and could release enough humidity to trigger a new ice age.

With the South Pole also moving into the interior of a continent at the same time the North Pole penetrated the enclosed Arctic, the earth's normal polar-tropical circulation of surface juices was restricted to an extreme degree — producing an effect similar to widening the spread of a thermostat switch until the furnace turn-on and shut-off temperatures are so far apart that the house (in this case, the earth) alternates between being too hot and too cold.

Such a complex state of temperature-humidity oscillation, of course, may well continue until the earthly poles, prodded by weight shifts between glacier and sea, work their way back into ocean regions of larger circulation. For obviously all it takes to start a glacier is a slight unmelted residue of spring snow at the time of the first autumn flurries in an average year. As long as there is just that slight net gain of the white patch from one year to the next, the glacier will grow, and precipitation out of humid air is surely as vital a factor as coolness in creating it. This is shown by the presence of glaciers on the equator in humid spots like Ecuador, New Guinea and even around Lake Victoria in hottest central Africa, while dry northern Alaska, northern Siberia, and the northernmost tip of Greenland, where it now seldom snows, have no glaciers at all.

But the largest lag factor affecting ice-age rhythms seems to be the amazing insulation of the terrestrial oceans as a whole — oceans which today still retain much of the coolth of the last glacial period in their depths, being sometimes below the freezing point of fresh water along their bottoms and averaging close to 32° F. throughout, despite much greater warmth at most places on the sunny surface, to say nothing of the immense heat of the underlying basalt. This present oceanic coldness inevitably inhibits salt-water evaporation, thereby retarding worldwide precipitation including snowfall, the raw material of glaciers. So in natural consequence, most ice areas are now waning. Yet in another twenty or thirty thousand years, when glaciers will presumably be only museum pieces, the ocean will have warmed enough so that evaporation will be faster, the skies cloudier, and — if man has not interfered too much with his dense population and chemical, atomic, space, solar, and other technologies — snowfall may have increased to the point of tipping the balance and launching the next ice age. Other factors like sunspots and volcanic dust in the atmosphere, the rise of mountain chains and anomalies of global motion undoubtedly have their effects, but geophysicists still seem unable to establish their relative importance.

The circulation of the oceans, of course, like the freer, faster flowing of the atmosphere, is one of the great components of earthly environment. Like a vast engine driven by the thermodynamic need for exchange between the cool polar condenser regions and the warm equatorial boiler belt, the oceans circulate partly in vertical fronts of different tempered water masses and partly in great revolving horizontal gyres wherever they find room, the centers of their surface whirls, like the semistagnant Sargasso Sea, being displaced toward the west by the torque effect of the earth's turning, thus intensifying currents on the western sides of oceans: the Gulf Stream, the Japanese Current, the Brazil, the Agulhas . . . And these currents are much more complex than they used to seem, not only changing their courses daily but habitually sloughing into separate filaments, some of which form loops that tear completely loose and roll off to the sides as capricious eddies hundreds of miles in diameter. Other

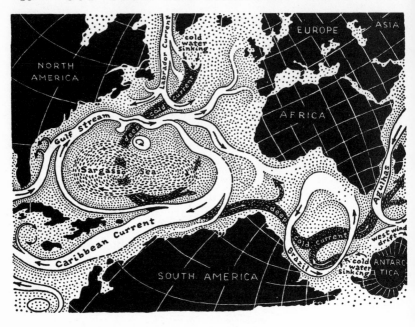

cooler currents from the Arctic and Antarctic slink some two miles under the better-known surface streams, carrying icy glacier run-off water toward the equator, bearing rich microscopic nutrients to deep, black "deserts" where fish would starve without them, carving great subsea valleys, in some places cutting steep canyons a thousand miles long like the one running south from Greenland, in others indenting great plains studded with 20,000-foot submarine volcanoes. More than five hundred examples of a weird variety of such volcanoes have been recently discovered on the Pacific floor in the form of truncated cones called guyots. These have internal veins like plants through which they once sprouted slowly with lava sap, but they are now dormant and flat-topped, perhaps from surf-action during some intermediate atoll stage before the elevation and draining of the present continents deepened the oceans to their existing levels.

The reason for the somewhat greater total flow of ocean water toward the equator than toward the poles seems to be the excess of evaporation over precipitation in the earth's doldrum belt of greatest heat as contrasted with the reverse condition in the cloudier temperate latitudes. But if rain can thus stir the seas, how much more does the wind influence the water below it, pushing and sucking the waves along, especially the little ripples that oceanographers have lately discovered are far more efficient than the bigger waves in absorbing energy from the sky — like the atoms, making up in coordination and numbers what power they lack as individuals.

The total circulation of the atmosphere is also more important than sea motion in giving life, for it refreshes the entire world, bringing aeration to the oceans and breath and drinks to mosses, mosquitoes, muskrats and men. But like the earth's more solid parts, the air too shares in evolution. It was not always fit for breath. Chemical deduction suggests that when our home globe was very young and hot, the atmosphere was mostly ammonia fumes mixed with wild gassy compounds of bromine, chlorine, fluorine or sulfur. The blend was, in fact, too violent to last. The atomic fury of the temperature could not be held down by earthly gravity, and almost all this primordial witches' brew escaped, to be slowly replaced on the cooling surface with milder volcanic gases that belched from the simmering rocks: preponderantly carbon dioxide, water vapor, and nitrogen.

While the earth cooled enough to condense its water vapor into oceans, oxygen was increasing through the chemical impact of sunlight upon the water (containing oxygen) and later upon green plants that had absorbed carbon dioxide from the pristine air. And thus evolved our present atmosphere, continually spooned with warm updrafts and centrifugal momentums into the yeasty pattern of jet streams, rolling frontal storms, monsoons, tradewinds, hurricanes and cells of circulation that we are beginning to know today. Only "beginning" to know, because the terrestrial atmosphere with its incomprehensible currents, its sporadic domes and dales of pressure and humidity, its chemical and magnetic layers, is far too big to be adequately observed while the ratio remains of two million tons of air to each man, woman and child on earth.

Yet significantly, if not forebodingly, man has already had an influence on this great gassy envelope — as indeed on the solid surface beneath it — an influence largely inadvertent but in cumulative effect unmistakable. In fact, this human influence must presage something deeply fundamental to the earth, being an event suddenly and utterly new on a planet that has seemingly tried everything in its five billion years. Perhaps it does not look like much to you down there in the traffic and bustle of Earth, but I assure you any detached scholar can see it with half an eye from up here. And it has become clear as space itself in the past fifty years.

Before that, one might have shrugged the manprints off as just a passing phase of old-fashioned earthly nature: the forests of China that suddenly looked moth-eaten a few millenniums ago, then almost completely vanished as from the plague; the valleys of Mesopotamia and the Nile that began to break out in specks of spring green; the strips of harvest yellow that have slowly spread like a creeping moss over the fertile plains.

But now look what is happening. The dots of cities have begun to accelerate outward and many a newly green valley has already been swallowed whole by masonry and twinkling lights! It looks as if concrete and electricity are more alive than vegetation and new lakes are appearing like blue blossoms in every continent, great rivers changing their courses, wide deserts receiving water where such luxury has not been seen in ten million years, and more and more strange arterial lines being scratched each year across the plains. Certainly this is a startling jolt in the leisurely pace of natural evolution.

Even the color of the air is changing, along with its chemistry, as smoke and carbon dioxide pour into it in tiny but multiplying streams. I can see the smoggy wisps floating in a hundred valleys where they were unknown before this century. I've even noticed unnatural rain clouds suddenly sprouting as if man at last had really learned to sow the seeds of weather. And what is this: this unprecedented volley of explosive fury, these potent flashes in the desert and on lonely ocean isles followed by mushroom clouds a hundred miles across? Whose are these new darts of life rising completely out of the air to challenge the meteors of black space? Even a few rash upstart rivals of our ancient moon, like the very sky station I am riding?

Is it a disease that has come to our good earth? Is mankind a virus bred to conquer his host organism in a fever of delirium, or is he just part of a healthy mold that must flower on all suitable planetary clay? Is he a fluke of fate or a phase of life?

I am here to seek the answer. I too sprang from that world down there, and am still part of it, even as this fleeing space station — even as the devoted moon. I am of the race that dwelt in Karnak and Jarmo and Jericho and Chichen Itza and Cnossus — in Olduvai Gorge and the Dragons' Mountain. My body was shaped in the rivers where vertebrates developed and the lung was born. My apprenticeship was in the trees where I grew my hand. I was once Proconsul, the pre-man. After the uplifting of the continents produced the grassy fields, I learned to stand up and look far and to outthink the lion.

In this day I have walked on the shoulders of the Pharaohs as they walked on the shoulders of the apes, for each page of history along with its cities must sink literally beneath the pavings of the future, even as I in my turn will lie buried under the scriptures of rocks today unformed.

If my honored ancestors once arose from sea to land and into the air, is it not my turn now to move onward beyond air into space? For I am also the creature that learned to weigh stars. I have seen the world in a puddle dry up one day and begin elsewhere the next. I know that any world may die and be born and that my own world has shown signs of being the cell of a greater life. I accept as man's normal business: to reach for the sun, to build things reachable out of things unreachable. Yet before reaching out with my hand I reach out with my mind — a human mind which can pass through the hottest fire and the blackest space — a mind which has never been taught to shun the moon or to fear the stars — and which has, for a reason still unknown, been endowed with a swiftness greater than light.

2. into the
stomach of space

AT FIRST THE BLACKNESS OF THE VOID that swallows us out here seems empty — a clear crystalline vacuum. Yet acquaintance steadily endows it with a certain tangibleness, a mysterious and subtle palpability that hardly touches the senses while deeply penetrating the mind.

This it may be that the young physicists are excited about when they say space is "chuck-full" of things: of waves and fields and magnetic properties, of energy both positive and negative, and even of hard-to-measure "particles" mingled with hard-to-believe "antiparticles" acting along lines of invisible curvature.

We will be looking closely at the texture and inner nature of such things in the second part of this book, but first we must just learn to use space a little, to live with it as a medium of travel into the great outside world, to savor it as a frame of material existence and as the surround of our floating home which it somehow harbored long before we earthbound bar-

barians ever came to recognize it as the newest frontier of our provincialism.

As Goethe once said of the institution of marriage, "The possible will be attempted only because we have postulated the impossible." So, I think, must the enormous possibilities of space be dared for the very reason that "flying to the moon" has been proverbially impossible through all history up to now. Certainly one need embrace this burgeoning age of rocketry with heart as well as mind, just as did the ancient Phoenicians and Greeks accept the advent of great ships along with harpies and sea monsters and boiling maelstroms — as later Henry the Navigator launched the age of organized discovery upon downhill oceans and islands haunted with dangerous simurgs and werewolves and mermaids. If Columbus somehow succeeded against all the vaunted hazards and superstitious yarns of sailors, so must we. If Galileo be remembered longer than the threats of the vested and the scoffings of the orthodox, and after him Fulton, Pasteur and the Wright brothers, so yet may we too accomplish deeds that are bigger than doubts.

Science fiction is obviously today's legend of space and in its turn is being overtaken by research scientists and hard-headed engineers who, like Ulysses, have firmly bound themselves to the mast of fact against the worst wiles of the sirens of fancy. Although the austerity of their lives on the stark deserts of White Sands, Alamogordo, Muroc, the steppes of Russia or the beaches of Canaveral may be relieved in some cases by reading about the magnetic, methane-breathing nereids of Neptune, today at last the inventors are filling out our ancient dreams with tangible hardware. And common people, no longer snickering at literal moon rockets or vehicles for Venus, are now urging the engineers to hurry, anticipating an accelerating success with "space suits" for their children, even devouring a whole new wave of literature on the already classic subject.

This literature had a beginning at least as far back as the second century A.D. when Lucian of Samosata wrote about a man whose ship sailed beyond the Pillars of Hercules and at the edge of the world was picked up by a waterspout and carried to the moon. In Lucian's second book, the now experienced hero borrowed two wings, one from a vulture, the other from an eagle, and took off for the moon from Mount Olympus. It was a day in which flying through the air was considered the same thing as space travel and some people believed it logical that birds could really migrate to the stars.

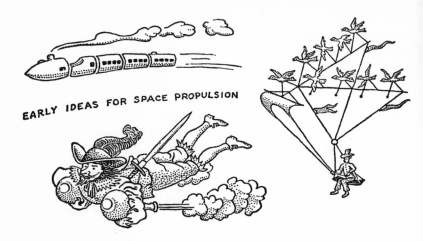

EARLY IDEAS FOR SPACE PROPULSION

So far as I am aware, the next book on space — appearing 1,500 years later — was written by the greatest astronomer of his time, Johannes Kepler, who realized that wings needed air, which probably did not extend all the way to the moon, and therefore used demonic propulsion as a less implausible means of getting his hero there. Since his own mother had been indicted as a witch and magic was still popular science even among the educated, demons seemed real enough. But Kepler's description of the moon, at least, was based on his own startling observations by telescope and had a profound influence on later writers (including Cyrano de Bergerac, whose *Histoire comique ou Voyage dans la Lune* was published in 1650) right up to the present century.

It would be almost impossible to read or even count the vast writings, mostly fiction, that have appeared about space travel since the development of aviation brought us to its threshold. But now actual accomplishment in current news reports is crowding fiction into the background. Earth-built rockets are part of the celestial firmament. They have become satellites of the earth and the sun and have landed on the moon, while man himself is following closely, having accepted this ultimate vehicle as easily as the balloon, the parachute or the airplane. In point of fact, the rocket far antedates them all. For it is actually an ancient Chinese invention, was used against the attacking Mongols in the siege of Kaifeng in A.D. 1232 and incidentally contributed the famous "red glare" to American skies in the War of 1812. But it remained little more than a psychological weapon and a plaything until World War II. Then it suddenly zoomed into rapid development. Although 1940 had seen no man-made rocket ever move as fast as 1,000 m.p.h., by 1950 several had exceeded 5,000 m.p.h. and before 1960 had reached an astounding 25,000 m.p.h. in outer space, demonstrating the possibility of crossing the Atlantic in half an hour, seeing sunrises in the west, sunsets in the east, stars by day, sunshine by night, and other miracles of wind, temperature and light. The highest altitude achieved by man-made devices increased still more rapidly: from about 10 miles in 1940 to 250 miles before 1950 and, by 1960, with the conquest of earthly gravitation fully attained, there seemed no limit whatever.

This explosion of material progress has been too fast for average human intuition, however, so that missile firings are hard to believe even when you see them, and all rocket doings still seem to me like staged drama. Before a major shoot, the launching site is alive with scurrying jeeps and trucks and figures clad in chemical-proof abas, some with earphones or walkie-talkie radios, some on servicing towers pumping hydrazine or giving rocket "brains" their final intelligence tests while radar mirrors sweep the sky with pulsed electronic beams, and the glassy eyes of cameras, telescopes and theodolites look on coolly from neighboring beaches or mountainsides. The dozens of human jet-age stargazers waiting around for the zero hour of launching then always remind me of the faithful shepherds of similar deserts in the ancient Holy Land who have long had an equally great faith that the world can be changed. Even though on the face of it the two kinds of change are different, I think they are also profoundly related in a way that will one day be made manifest to all.

   Those who think man is becoming overbold in this rash tampering with physical evolution have, of course, a powerful argument in the extreme and multiple dangers of such a change of worlds for which the human body is obviously not genetically prepared. Certainly the artificial haste of man's leap is far from precedented anywhere in earthly history. Biologists point with trembling fingers to the contrast between it and the way the fish so successfully colonized the land against similar difficulties. During many painful and frustrating eons of struggle to conquer a deadly new medium, the air, inevitably the fish suffered frightful losses as their heroic pioneers were stranded by receding tides and suffocated or baked alive in marshy deltas, trying to keep their vital juices from drying up in the blistering, blinding outer sunshine — just as space doctors are now trying to perfect space suits that will protect men's blood and lungs and skin and brains against the glaring vacuum and radiations of space. But little by little, through relentless genetic variation and selection, the fish developed a tough air suit that not only enabled them to carry their own traditional sea environment to land with them but filtered out the dangerous parts of the spectrum of sunlight and stabilized their temperature sea-fashion within narrow limits despite the fickle winds and the daily and seasonal freezes and roasts of the cruel airy world. The sudden and unexpected load of a full G (earthly gravitational unit) of unsupported weight in "empty" air of course left the soft-muscled ones flattened helplessly on the beaches, as jellyfish often are marooned to this day, but gradually the most elite of the elite new breeds grew powerful antigravity muscles and air gills called lungs and held themselves up off the ground and at last even shifted into high gear with legs and wings.

Thus laboriously and extravagantly did nature accomplish in millions of years the equivalent of what man now seems bent on accomplishing in one generation. No wonder there are few responsible scientists who are optimistic about a full-scale conquest of space in this century. The only tolerable space suit now guaranteed for more than brief use is a solid walled chamber with full insulation, air conditioning and mechanical limbs, for no body-contour suit yet developed seems able to provide enduring flexibility without serious risks of loss of pressure, to say nothing of insufficient insulation. The human body demands at least three pounds per square inch of air or oxygen pressure around it, which the space suit must unfailingly provide. Any leak threatens immediate death. Moisture and carbon dioxide given off must of course be disposed of and oxygen and temperature maintained — these being services which for only a few hours require more apparatus than a man alone can practically handle, especially if he is expected to be able to concentrate on a dangerous and unfamiliar world outside his clothing.

But do not think this tough problem will not be licked sooner or later. If the fish could do it, who are we to quit? As surely as we are the cousins, if not the descendants, of the very most successful of all the most daring of fish, space is within human reach. Man knows it in his soul. None of the rocket scientists has expressed doubt about complete victory, even though the cost in lives and heartbreaks and years cannot be foreseen, nor the many losing and winning combinations of devices and techniques.

Out of the legions of engineers and researchers every year new prophets of space arise to point the way in confident voices — sensationally successful young men like Wernher von Braun of V2 fame, who has been compared to Peter the Hermit and who explains his faith in words Peter might have used in defending the visionary paupers' crusade: "Prophets have always been laughed at, deplored and opposed, but some prophets have proved to be following the true course of history."

If this be mystical, at least von Braun's expressed ambition of going as far as the moon in person before he is through is human and natural. And his original plan for constructing a fleet of three-stage ferry rockets, each as big as a sixteen-story building, with which to reach a satellite orbit and there put together a permanent settlement of dwellings, observatories, shops and assembly plants, had a practical earthy realism about it — even though it added up to being a blueprint of the first space town in human history (very likely in solar-system history as well) and which would drift blithely along at more than 4 miles a second some 1,075 miles above the earth. Admittedly, the work and expense involved in teaching such 180-foot rockets to fly and fly with precision and reliability, each carrying eleven tons of payload high enough to lay the cornerstone of a brand-new "moon" and safely return, amounted to a major national project. For as surely

as Mount Everest required a hundred men to get two men to the top, the conquest of space requires many thousandfold more.

Indeed, such a thing grows by geometric progression. Just as elephants are more complicated than fleas because they are larger, not larger because they are more complicated, so a three-stage rocket (large because it must contain a hundred tons of fuel for each ton of cargo) has its special motors to work its large controls, its little fuel pumps that pump fuel to drive its big fuel pumps, its hydraulic systems and electronic feedbacks, its radar recorders and gyro potentiometers and servo motors and assorted safety gadgets and accelerometers and pressure gauges and governors *ad confuseam.*

Von Braun has worked out a full-dress invasion of Mars which at present would cost about the same as fighting a fair-sized war and, he thinks, will be a welcome substitute when wars are "a thing of the past." Several dozen of his destroyer-size (1,410-ton) three-stage rockets must make about 400 ferry trips up more than a thousand miles from the earth to build and stock the large satellite assembly plant and service station there, from which a squadron of two 1,870-ton "orbit-to-orbit" space ships (a passenger vessel and a freighter) will be prepared and sent to Mars with fourteen men. Arriving at the gravity gate of the red planet after 260 days of high-speed sailing, the astronauts will build a Martian mooring and service station (perhaps on one of Mars' tiny moons) and equip it with "landing craft" for taking nine men down to the planet itself for a full year of exploration.

The scientific know-how for accomplishing this is already at hand, says von Braun. Gravity is no longer an uncontrollable or monstrous force. Man is already big enough for interplanetary travel and is definitely committed to it with appropriations already provided. The plan is actually in process as part of the American man-in-space program and it may be expected to come into operation this century in some period when Mars is in favorable proximity to the earth. Now it is largely a matter of making more tests, getting used to the moon, cooperating more closely with the Russians if possible, building large stocks of high-quality equipment and doing a lot of unprecedented human engineering.

As for gravity, although it is still one of the great mysteries of nature, man has learned how to use it to his advantage just as he has learned to use steam, electricity and the atom in varying degrees. To be sure, gravity has opposed his departure from Earth with a stubborn terrestrial jealousy, but he has discovered it is not so fierce as it used to seem and that once gravity is about to be breached it relaxes into an amazing docility. In fact, of all the realms of scientific progress "nothing succeeds like success" in the sky. At 12,000 miles above the earth a "pound weight" weighs only an ounce. The higher you go the easier you go, even though gravity never disappears entirely in the known universe.

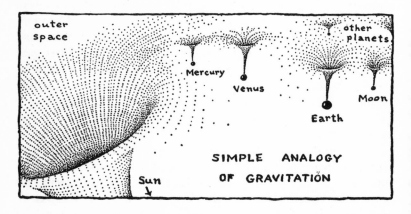

SIMPLE ANALOGY OF GRAVITATION

Perhaps the most helpful analogy about gravity from the viewpoint of rocket crewmen venturing into space is to think of gravitational fields as remote whirlpools in the calm ocean of emptiness that lies between the stars. On the mirror-smooth "surface" of space there is virtually no strain nor turbulence nor friction — just clear sailing in any direction — except in those rare maelstroms created by the moon, the planets and the stars.

Space journeying, in fact (as far as gravitation is concerned), would be as simple as a calm sea voyage on earth did we not live in the very center of one of these gravity whirlpools. The space engineers describe ours (which is typical) as funnel-shaped and 4,000 miles deep, because "the work of getting away from the earth is exactly the same as would be needed to climb vertically through a distance equal to the radius of the earth" if gravity all the way up were just as it is at sea level.

Of course this analogy is an oversimplification, because gravity is not everywhere the same, nor is it whirling literally, and it extends upward far beyond 4,000 miles — in fact, never ends entirely, according to Newton's famous law or Einstein's refinement of it. The reason for describing the gravity field as having a funneloid or (more precisely) helicoidal-trumpet shape is only that such a form approximately expresses the change with altitude, and is easy to visualize — though actual gravity is something much more profound, as we shall see later on in this book.

The climb is naturally very tough up the nearly vertical walls at the bottom of any large gravity whirlpool but, when you have built up enough impetus to reach the gentler slopes above, it takes only a little more to come out completely onto the flat ocean surface where you can just relax and coast indefinitely. If you can't quite make it straight out of the whirlpool, however, you need not give up. There is still the alternative of changing your course to a spiral, an ellipse or a circle — of at least holding your own against gravity by going rapidly around and around the maelstrom instead of directly up it. That is exactly what you would probably do if caught in a real whirlpool, and that is what the captive moon does in the whirlpool of earthly gravity. It is the principle of the "Wall of Death," the old carnival sideshow stunt in which a motorcyclist defies gravity by riding fast around the almost vertical walls inside a cylindrical tower built like a silo with a bowl-shaped bottom.

The specific value of this trick to defeat gravity is that although an initial speed of about 25,000 m.p.h. (about 7 miles a second) is needed to coast from the earth straight up, you can do with much less by taking off eastward from the equator, thus gaining a free boost from the earth's horizontal spin of 1,000 m.p.h. at that latitude and continuing to slant up eastward until clear of air friction. At about two hundred miles up, as the satellite rockets have already demonstrated, a horizontal speed of a mere 5 m.p.s. is enough to keep you from falling back to Earth — and you have thus become a private "moon" on a "free orbit." At an altitude of 25,000 miles, you can stay up at only 2 m.p.s. and your orbit can be even freer. It may be a swooping orbit like a comet's or a nearly circular orbit like the moon's. It makes little difference so long as you stay above air and have attained the necessary angular momentum. Getting completely out of the whirlpool is, relatively speaking, a push-over from here. The rule is that from any orbit that holds you continuously above the earth (or above any other gravitating body) all you need do is multiply your velocity by the square root of 2 to escape the body altogether. Thus, if any satellite with an average velocity of 2 m.p.s. increases it to $2\sqrt{2}$, or 2.8 m.p.s., it will just sail off never to return.

Of space's many weird problems, the navigation or astrogation one is particularly interesting to those of us who have so long flitted about the easy earth. Have you ever wondered how you would find your way between the worlds? Or what it might feel like to be "lost" while in plain sight of your destination because of doubt as to which way either you or your destination were going? Earth maps are mostly in two dimensions, even though some of them attempt to portray the contours of the land as well as suggest the curvature of the sphere. But space is definitely at least three-dimensional. How does a space navigation chart look?

The answer is that, strictly speaking, charts will not be used for space navigation, mainly because plotting on a chart is much too crude a procedure for the fine precision that is essential in outer three-dimensional space. As my friend Professor Samuel Herrick, astronomer and founder of the Institute of Navigation, puts it, "Whereas navigating to the nearest minute of arc is adequate for sea and air navigation, in space we shall have to take account of the second of arc, or even smaller fractions of it. That will require six or seven decimal places in calculation, and . . . you may be sure that all space navigation will be done with calculating machines instead of charts."

The basic reason for such a standard of accuracy in space of course is not alone the obvious one that the tiniest error in aim at departure from Earth may amount to missing a planet such as Venus by many thousands of miles five months later unless corrected, perhaps at great expense, but also that space ships (like all celestial bodies) follow orbits, not straight lines. For it takes six mathematical quantities to define the position and velocity of the ship at any moment: the three coordinates of its location in three-dimensional space and the three components of its velocity in the same 3-D frame of reference, every one of the six being subject to constant change even when the ship is just drifting.

If you don't think this is complexity requiring electronic help, you need only consider it carefully in relation to more familiar situations like flying an airplane about the earth. Down there in the terrestrial atmosphere, if you know your location accurately even in only two dimensions (latitude and longitude), you have practically solved your navigation problem, for your position in the third dimension (altitude) is confined within narrow limits and easy to determine, and your velocity components are also so restricted and normally so controllable that you hardly need know them except to help in reckoning your latitude and longitude.

But here in space there is no kind of surface constantly available for reference in finding your bearings, and your cruising speed may vary not just fifty percent from, say, 400 to 600 m.p.h., but can range many thousand percent from a fraction of a mile per second up to more than 50 m.p.s., without even considering the much greater speeds needed for travel beyond the solar system. Groundspeed as well as airspeed rapidly loses its meaning as you rise above the atmosphere, for you soon realize in space that different parts of the earth's surface are moving not only in different directions but at different speeds in relation to the rest of creation. Earthspeed (motion relative to the center of the earth) naturally becomes the new criterion of movement. Then, in turn, moonspeed, sunspeed, Marsspeed . . . The same goes for space coordinates, altitude inevitably growing into radial distance, rate of climb or descent into radial velocity, and latitudinal and longitudinal direction from the earth into solar or galactic latitude and longitude, and so on.

It is a relief not to have to worry any more about wind, a purely atmospheric phenomenon so far as we know, but, before you have time to sigh over this bounty, you realize with some shock that the curvature of space more than replaces wind as a navigation variable to contend with. And even though it is true that space distortion is more regular and predictable than any earthly gale, it is also more insidious and pervasive. In fact, space turns out to have a kind of geometric "pressure pattern" that is invisible, impalpable, immensely subtle and the very devil to keep track of.

While we must wait until Chapter 13 to go deeper into the basic nature of space, I can say here that space ships coasting along in what is called a state of "free fall" must always follow either an elliptical (closed) orbit or, if they are going faster, perhaps a hyperbolic (open) orbit for a brief time. In either case, it is literally true that there are no straight lines in space and it is not possible to steer a space ship in any ordinary sense. It is only

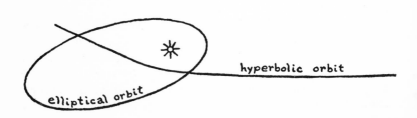

possible, by applying rocket thrust, to change it from one orbit to another. As astronomer J. G. Porter of the Royal Greenwich Observatory puts it, "even with unlimited supplies of fuel, in a ship which is constantly driven, it would still be impossible to travel in a straight line" — that being a course which does not exist.

Curves, then, must be accepted and dealt with as inevitable, like women in a man's world, tantalizing or troublesome though they may be. A way of easing the trouble, however, is to pre-compute your intended orbit along with a few substitute or emergency orbits and their appropriate conjunction seams of spheroidal surfaces of position (a calculation Dr. Porter says "is not going to be a nice job") while you are still on Earth with the best electronic computers at hand, so that in space, if all goes reasonably well, the navigation problem will be largely a matter of checking angles between sun, planets, moons and asteroids to see how closely they conform to the precomputed values.

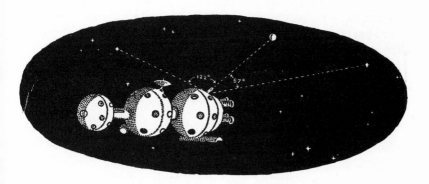

This vital work will be done with instruments now under in-tense development which presumably will combine the functions of the filar micronometer, the electronic star tracker, the gyro-stabilized octant and the telescope. Obviously the traditional sextant, calibrated only to the minute of arc, is not nearly pre-cise enough in reading, say, Jupiter (85,000 miles across) as a point of light. Even the cross hairs of a good telescope, if aligned with the wrong part of Jupiter, might permit an error of 10,000 miles. Radio and radar instruments, of course, will supplement the visual ones, probably with elaborate bearing and range-measuring techniques similar in principle to the newest systems being installed in terrestrial airways to keep pilots constantly informed of the direction and distance to all stations around them — hence, by electronic transposition, of their own location.

While operating within a hundred thousand miles or so of a planet, moon or other body, such systems are particularly valuable and, when doppler radar is perfected to the point of making it possible to measure exact intervals between impulses, spacemen will also be able to read on a dial their speed of approach toward, or recession from, any substantial object within range. This is by no means the same thing as reading their "true velocity," but it can be at least an important clue at the crucial beginning and end of a journey.

And then, by feeding all the information obtainable into the space ship's miniature electronic brain, including the vital but hard-to-get data of velocity, the discrepancies between the precomputed values and the observed values can be digested and translated into terms of exact corrective maneuver — such as .58 G of thrust in the direction of galactic latitude 49°50′33″.6 south and longitude 12° 11′21″.0 east applied April 18 from 21:30:00 until 22:35:15 U.T.

Such a correction, of course, would mean a relatively small change of orbit, which would not appreciably reduce the fuel supply. But in a long interplanetary voyage, the big problem will be to keep corrective maneuvers small without letting them become frequent, since an error as tiny as 0.001 miles (five feet) per second in speed on a trip to Mars could make you miss the red planet by an embarrassing 50,000 miles.

And, even apart from errors, there are inevitable and drastic changes of orbit required in space travel, not only in accelerating away from a home space station at the start (partly to save travel time), but also, and more so, in matching velocities with your destination at the end. Some people seem to think space travel can be very economical as well as swift, but they probably fail to realize the enormous momentum possessed by a small space ship (weighing a few dozen tons) when it has built up a reasonable cruising speed of, say, 30 miles a second. Even though the space ship would weigh only a thousandth as much as an ocean liner like the *Queen Mary* it would still have the same momentum the *Queen Mary* had if she could move just one thousandth as fast as the space ship, or 108 miles an hour. If you can visualize now how much rocket fuel it would take to stop or turn the *Queen Mary* while she was hurtling through space at 108 m.p.h., you will know something of the basic problem of velocity blending which many astrophysicists believe must remain practically beyond the fuel capacity of any space ships at least until atomic or solar energy is fully developed as the power source for space. The strict relationship between maneuverability and weight is indicated by a missile engineer's recent calculation that chemically propelled space ships on heliocentric orbits must consume about 3 percent of their total weight in fuel every time they change their orbits by as much as five minutes of arc.

The difficulty here is inherent also in the varied order of the celestial orbs which, like the earthly oceans before them, still show little sign of having been created for the purpose of simplifying the struggles of humanity. The orbits of even our nearest planetary neighbors, for example, are not in the same plane as the earth's. And even though a space ship could be put into an "optimum" orbit that is roughly tangent to those of both the earth and, say, Venus at opposite ends of its elliptical shape, its velocity would require about as much fuel and power to match the velocity of its destination at either end as it had consumed in climbing away from the earth in the first place — and this assumes very accurate timing throughout and no errors.

There is obviously only one time a year (not an earth year but a composite year averaged from those of the two planets) when this optimum orbit is obtainable: the time when one planet overtakes the other on their way around the sun. When a circus rider jumps from one horse to a passing one while they gallop around the ring, he naturally leaps just before the moment of greatest proximity and lands just after it. So will the space navigators plan a journey to Venus: departing when Venus is almost a sixth of a turn behind the earth and arriving after she has passed it by almost the same margin, their chosen optimum orbit bringing their ship from aphelion (the orbit's farthest point from the sun) as it leaves the earth through 250 million miles and 146 days to perihelion (closest point to sun) at Venus in such a natural manner that were it to just miss Venus through engine trouble at velocity-matching time it would coast onward like a boomerang, circling around to the departure point on the earth's orbit again in another 146 days, another 250 million miles.

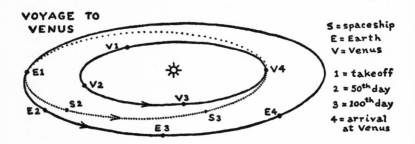

VOYAGE TO VENUS

S = spaceship
E = Earth
V = Venus

1 = takeoff
2 = 50th day
3 = 100th day
4 = arrival at Venus

Of course, its navigator could not expect to find the earth there this time, for you Earthians would then be some 120 million miles behind the space ship (having traveled a longer path) and still going away. In fact, he would not come within ten million miles of Earth again until his fifth time around, 5 space-ship years after departure (4 earth years or 6⅔ Venus years). If he had enough air, water and supplies to hold out that long, he could have taken another crack at Venus at his third perihelion, though more likely he would be saving everything for what would probably be his last and only chance to get back to — you guessed it; there's no place quite like it — home.

Of course, if a space ship had efficient atomic motors and no problem about running out of fuel, it could overcome almost any difficulty of a missed rendezvous by just turning on the power and chasing its destination until it caught it. Or it could take a short cut home, not by the slow, economical elliptical orbit route but by the daring hyperbolic course of a plunge downward past the sun and out on the other side. This would be very extravagant in fuel, involving the radical maneuver of almost complete cancellation of lateral planetary motion, but it would save a lot of time because the ship would pick up enormous speed in its drop toward the sun just as a comet does. Although such an unconservative course might be likened to crossing from one skyscraper tower to another in New York by direct cable instead of by the more leisurely route of taking an elevator to the ground level and walking across the street, then up in another elevator, the method may some day become very important in voyages to the outer planets such as Jupiter, Saturn and Neptune, which would otherwise consume much if not most of the passengers' lifetimes. It has been calculated that if the space ship adds still more to its speed past the flaming sun by using up most of its remaining fuel, this will not only give it tremendous momentum but, lightening its load, make it shoot upward toward Neptune with such great rapidity that its crew can forget their problem of how to pass the weary years, occupying themselves instead with the urgency of slamming on their brakes before it is too late.

The long-range space and time relationships in all such voyages are quite satisfactorily found by solving the equations used in what is known in space mechanics as the "two-body problem." That is the relatively simple consideration of how two bodies move while influenced by nothing other than their own mutual gravitational attraction, the two bodies normally being the space ship and the sun.

But of course the near approach to another planet will require answers from the much more difficult "three-body problem" and, where even this closer approximation to reality is insufficient, from "perturbation theory" (which treats all gravitational influences beyond the third body as "perturbations"), integrating larger influences by Cowell's method, smaller periodic ones by

Encke's, and so on. Most of such more advanced "astroga-tional" work will probably be done as part of the electronic precomputation on Earth from where, in emergencies, it may prove helpful as a special "trouble-shooting service" that will forward key corrections by radio or heliograph to the naviga-tor in space.

In any case, one does not need to get bogged down with more details of space navigation at this elementary stage of as-tronautics. If we must be swallowed by space, let us not succumb to its bile before we have even noticed the contents of its stomach. Let us attend to the near at hand and take nature in digestible doses — one world at a time — so that we may hope to know at least where we are.

3. invitation to the moon

THAT PALE ORB OF ROCK swinging around the earth seems to me to have significance beyond what humanity has generally accorded it. Although only an incidental decoration to many, a sky festoon to the romantic, the moon is nevertheless a lucid example of natural law beyond our home world, a daily demonstration that a stone weighing 81,000,000,000,000,000,000 tons can be made to float indefinitely 240,000 miles overhead without visible means of support.

She is also the earth's closest relative, high arbitress of Easter and an unmistakable celestial personality who invites candid comment. Though not extremely old, neither is she young. Even from here, one can plainly see her history written in wrinkles. Yet we must admit that she is rounded and beautiful, clear-cut of character, and faithful in many such time-honored duties as accompanying the terrestrial traveler on long journeys despite his passing of trees and houses, hills and clouds. And she is always punctual in appointment, ever facing the earth directly — in fact, amazingly regular once you understand her devious ways.

This is not to say she is without mystery either as to the un-documented features of her past or the enigmatic present hidden within her countenance and behavior that are at once familiar and unearthly. How often I remember from my days with the airlines, cruising under a broken overcast to see the moon stealthily shouldering her way between cumulus masses — a tigress skulking in the jungle. Or when she was crescent, watching her cleave the cirrus with her scimitar blade. Or gibbous, becoming a bowl of porridge under the nimbus steam.

Sometimes it is hard to realize, when the moon seems un-imaginably far away, that there are cars on the roads of Earth that have been driven farther — that in space 240,000 miles is only arm's length. Yet obviously, at 240 m.p.h. that distance is covered in 1,000 hours of flying time. At 2,400 m.p.h. in 100 hours. Some airline pilots have done twenty times as much: the full equivalent of ten round trips to the moon.

If the moon is not literally arm's length away, she is actually within the stretch of your body. Someone has calculated that the average human arteries hold about 24,000,000,000,000 red blood cells which, laid edge to edge, would stretch 116,000 miles. If you added all your white corpuscles and, if necessary, stored up some extra blood in a personal bank, you could expect the blood of your own body to be easily enough to reach the moon.

The moon might appreciate some new blood too, for her future never looked less secure. Not only has she already felt the rude jab of an earthly missile, without so much as a per-functory "May I?" but growing numbers of eager Earthians down there, who like to talk about being good neighbors, have already filed claims to sections of her land and begun arguing about carving it up to their personal ends.

Besides, millions of men have long been reading their private superstitions and pet "man in the moon" meanings into the suggestive markings of the moon's bright mountains and dark plains. Did you know that from India people see in the moon not a man but a little gray rabbit with long ears and outstretched paws? Perhaps this is nearly the same as the moon goblin Puritan mothers used to show their children, which had a wart on its nose and held scissors for snipping off the tongues of those who sassed their parents. In Samoa they see a moon lady who sits up there eternally weaving a nebulous cloth into clouds, while other South Sea natives see moon trees laden with fruit for eternal feasting of departed souls. The Indians of the American northwest envision a horned toad that hopped to the moon to get away from a wolf. Other tribes see a duck there. Still others, a spread eagle. In Australia some see a staring cat's eye, while the French recognize the wicked face of Judas Iscariot. And Irish maidens, after drinking white wine and rose water, look at the moon through silk handkerchiefs to see the faces of their personal fates, murmuring,

> I prithee, good Moon, declare to me
> This night, who my husband shall be.

In olden terrestrial days the moon was mainly a divine feminine influence, a glamorous goddess of fertility, often a very down-to-earth personality. Take Selene, the Greek moon, who was wooed by King Zeus and by Pan in the shape of a white ram, and who loved Endymion so much that she put him to sleep on Mount Latmus so she could kiss him secretly as she set each night. The result of the latter lunar indulgence over many years was the birth of full fifty moon daughters — thirty-one of whom have already been converted from legendary figures into actual planetary satellites as they were discovered by Galileo, Cassini, Herschel, Nicholson (four each) and other recent astronomers, variously circulating in moonly devotion around Mars, Jupiter, Saturn, Uranus and Neptune. (See the moon table on pages 62–63.)

Our modern moon, of course, outshines all ancient ones a

hundredfold in wonder and romantic potential. She was our earliest celestial destination. She was the first outside world to echo radio impulses sent from the earth into space. She is a mirror who reflects both sunlight and earthlight to our sight just as our world returns moonshine along with sunshine to her, so that one glance at the dark side of the new moon apprises us of the weather for thousands of miles westward where the whiteness of wide cloudy areas is earthshine's main source. She is the place where all of us see morning during the night, where her slow afternoon stretches into our dawn. She holds the power of appearing paradoxically larger when she is rising or setting than when she is 4,000 miles nearer overhead.

Astronomers think of the moon as a kind of clock — an ancient timepiece that helped eighteenth-century navigators check their longitude, a clock that moves reliably before the stars at the rate of about one diameter (32′ of arc) every forty minutes of time, a clock whose face is the map of history telling the story of a violent youth and of a sterile maturity — up till now. Rocket men see in the moon a way-station to the solar system, a future refueling base for satellite tankers, a navigation check-point after takeoff for the planets.

The moon is all of these things — and more. If you look at her through a telescope you can pick out an amazing landscape, its meaning in part instantly obvious but also in part inscrutable even after careful study. Her face may remind you first of a smallpox victim. Or an old artillery ground. You can make out crater heaped upon crater, in some places tiny craters showing in larger craters which in turn rise out of still larger ones. One peak of the Leibniz mountains soars four thousand feet higher than Mount Everest and is located near the northern lunar pole amid the so-called "mountains of eternal light" which never withdraw from clear sunshine no matter how the moon's face is turned. Clavius, the largest crater of all on the visible moon, has been measured at 146 miles across, making it bigger than Massachusetts, Connecticut and Rhode Island combined. In fact, it is so big in relation to the tight curvature of the moon that if you stood in the middle of Clavius it would appear as an endless plain receding in all directions, for the 20,000-foot mountains surrounding you would be hidden well below the horizon.

Astronomers and selenographers (who study the moon as geographers study the earth) do not all agree as to whether moon craters are meteorite scars or ancient volcanoes or perhaps even rings left by bursting bubbles of gas, but the best present opinion is that almost all of them were made by meteorites. The volcanic theory was based largely on the weak gravity of the moon, which not only can attract relatively fewer meteorites than the earth but would allow bigger volcanic eruptions from which the lava would be hurled much higher and farther than on earth.

MOON CRATER   MT. VESUVIUS

Opposed to this idea, however, are the enormous sizes and depths of the craters, some of them a thousand times larger than any known terrestrial volcanic cones and many of them two miles deeper than the surrounding plains. There is also their unvolcanolike encroachment upon each other and their resemblance to artillery shell holes which similarly often have a small peak rising out of the center. In any case, the impact of tremendous ancient meteorites weighing many millions of tons or even small asteroids could explain just as well as volcanoes the pale marks radiating for thousands of miles outward from some of the craters, obviously produced by much more spectacular explosions than we have any record of on Earth. Lava flooding, of course, seems the likeliest explanation for the extensive dark "moon mares" where no craters are visible but which should also have received their portion of large meteorites throughout the earlier years of moon history. One theory has it that some of the last of the meteorites themselves released the lava by smashing the moon's crust, thus effectively flooding and concealing their own scars.

The earth also may have been as pocked as the moon in its early days with similar huge craters which have long since been eroded out. There is definite suspicion of a trace of just such a crater in a recent geological survey of northern Quebec, known as one of the most ancient parts of the dry earthly crust. And the very shapes of Hudson Bay, James Bay and Ungava Bay are highly suggestive.

But naturally, scars on the moon remain much longer than on the vegetating, restless earth, for without air to produce wind or clouds or rain or trees or streams there is almost nothing to change the moon's mountains. About the only possibility of erosion there that selenographers have figured out so far is the destructive expansion and contraction caused by the 400° F. temperature change between roasting day and deep-frozen night. The vacuum of course produces neither twilight nor insulation, and the coming of the first shadow at sunset brings an abrupt drop in temperature. And even more drastic is the effect of the swooping earth shadow when the earth passes exactly between the sun and moon — suddenly eclipsing the sun as seen from the moon, the moon as seen from the earth — producing a temperature plunge of 270° in one hour followed by a corresponding rise on the return of sunshine, an occurrence frequent and violent enough to cause major exfoliation of the moon's rocks over billions of years. Obviously, this eclipse-caused erosion can happen only on the one side of the moon that faces the earth, so, by deduction, we assume the other, less-eroded side is still rougher — as indeed the Russian photographic rocket of 1959 confirmed it to be.

It takes a little effort of imagination to think realistically of walking about on the moon— although it is not as hard as actually walking about on the moon — for the moon obviously cannot approach the earth in human-oriented hospitality. Much moonscape, in fact, is probably as bad as the Badlands of South Dakota or worse, though some of the lower levels may be covered with gravelly dust, perhaps many feet thick, that has worked down there from the crumbling cliffs and slopes. The feeble gravity would make up for some of the obstacles, of course, and crevasses no more than a hundred feet wide might be jumpable or sheer fifty-foot crater cliffs vaultable with practice. Tiny grain-sized meteorites may hit the ground intermittently like stray bullets out of the black sky, their velocity of dozens of miles per second virtually undiminished by atmosphere. The odd splashes of dust raised by these particles naturally do not form puffs and float as in air but fall downward with slow, steady acceleration. Nor do they make any noticeable sound, for silence prevails in the moon's vacuous calm of sublime desolation without weather, animals, birds, insects or vegetation visible anywhere. And overhead for fourteen earth days the sun blazes like a searchlight in the night surrounded by dazzling unblinking stars, while the great blue-white earth sits perpetually in one spot (never moving more than 7 degrees from its mean position), appearing fifteen times as big in area as the moon does on Earth and a hundred times brighter, yet never rising nor setting, just slowly revolving and, more slowly, going through its monthly phases from crescent to gibbous to full, ever exactly opposite and in perfect time with the moon's own corresponding changes.

The earth thus viewed through the refraction-free vacuum of space is always an awesome sight: its seas a darker, slightly greenish blue, its land pale-blue with tints varying from dull green to umber, from gray to red, and dramatically streaked in white around the equator with brilliant patches of stormy areas halfway to the dazzling poles. Certainly it is unique among planets in our solar system, being more than three quarters covered with water, a substance about as rare in the universe as a whole as emeralds are rare on earth. This general water scarcity is due both to the fact that oxygen forms much less than one percent of the total bulk of universal elements and to the fact that H_2O exists as water only in the narrow temperature range between freezing and boiling, while it remains ice throughout some 492 degrees (Fahrenheit) below freezing and steam for thousands of degrees (depending on surrounding pressure) above boiling before it splits into its separate elements.

It is therefore only the rare combination of chemistry and precise distance from a heat source (the sun), plus size and gravity sufficient to keep the elements from escaping into space, that permit the earth its dainty air and jewellike oceans — oceans that glisten in the sun as on no planet our telescopes can see, often showing that blinding highlight at some ocean spot where the sun is reflected with mirror clarity. As the clouds also constantly circulate with the winds, so our unique gem must slowly wink and blink as its lights dance from sea to cloud to forest to desert to cloud to sea, adding the magic of uncertain mood to the regular fluctuation of its revolvement.

If you wonder why only one face of the moon always looks toward the earth, which is also why the earth must hang almost stationary in the moon's sky, making the moon's day equal to its "month," it may be interesting to review the work of Sir George Darwin (son of the discoverer of earthly evolution), who has made more precise calculations of moon history (a beginning of celestial evolution) than anyone else I know of. The origin of the moon is still a matter of speculation, the leading theories favoring the idea that she either grew up with the infant earth separately from a common nebulous beginning, or that she burst from the earth just after the earth condensed into a globe — the expulsive force being one combination or another of centrifugal, tidal, volcanic and vibrational influences. Darwin's own calculations point to vibration as the key propellant. According to his theory, since the earth's longest natural vibration rate is about two hours, some four billion years ago when the day was only four hours long and solar tides in the earth therefore two hours apart, the sympathetic vibration naturally greatly amplified the tides. At one critical period of nearly perfect resonance that lasted some five hundred years, these tides presumably crescendoed to such overwhelming size that at the bulg-

ing molten equator of the then dizzily whirling earth enough
material lashed out into space to form the moon.

Other authorities, particularly Sir Harold Jeffreys, have since
shown by careful mathematics that such tides could have reached
a maximum height of not more than a couple of hundred miles
which would not have been enough to expel the moon — and
that therefore the moon must have been born before the earth
herself had entirely formed — at least as early as when they were
both in their primordial nebulous state of gas and dust. In which
case the moon was originally just the condensation of a gassy
filament extruded from the thin mother earth cloud by the tidal
force of the sun at a time when our planetary orbit was so
elongated that the mother cloud swooped like a comet, now
close to the sun, now way out toward the distant stars.

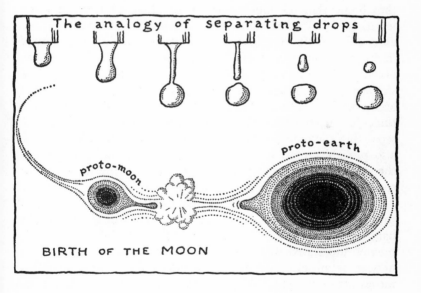

The analogy of separating drops

proto-earth

proto-moon

BIRTH OF THE MOON

On some such swing when the tidal period chanced to combine harmonically with the natural oscillation of the cloud, the
resonance must have reached a climax that plucked the tidal

wave of filament like a harp string, straining it beyond its elastic limit so that it snapped free and stayed just out of reach, revolving around and around the main cloud — a separate but still captive drop of Earth.

In basic accord with this idea was also that of Henri Poincaré, the mathematician and savant who, investigating the dynamics of spinning liquid spheres half a century ago, concluded that if such a ball accelerates "it must first distort itself doorknobwise, then develop a lop-sided equatorial bulge which at some magnitude of centrifugal force will finally extrude tangentially into a separate smaller body."

Whatever the actual facts of the moon's nativity, after she collected herself into a molten ball and settled into an orbit around the earth, her gradual development has become calculable backward from present observation to a reasonable nicety. Darwin thus found that the moon once upon a time evidently revolved less than 3,000 miles above our steaming skies as she whipped around her orbit in a four-hour month while the earth turned in its four-hour day, each keeping the same face toward the other, each daily eclipsing the other and raising tremendous stationary tides in material memory of the then fairly recent accouchement. But as the moon receded, she could not continue to keep up with the earth's turning and slipped behind, separating the month from the day while each period lengthened, also probably rotating slowly on her own axis independently — thereby setting up huge moving Earth tides on the lunar surface to match the great but lesser moon tides on earth.

It is of course these tides that have caused the moon to recede to her present remoteness, a result of the *push* of gravity that is hard for humans to understand while they remain so materially intoxicated with gravity's *pull*. For what you may have noticed as an apparent lag in the tides behind the moon as it moves across the sky is seen from our space-eye view as the rotation of the earth carrying the tides beyond the moon so that the tide crests stay just ahead (east) of the line joining the centers of earth and moon. This naturally tends to urge the moon perpetually onward (to the east) and, by thus increasing centrifugal force, to drive it outward — thereby creating a component of push induced by the tides of gravity!

But the same tides that urge the moon ahead, by the law of reaction, tend to hold the earth back, the friction of water against land over billions of years gradually absorbing some of the earth's energy and braking its rate of spin down to our present day. The very large tides on the moon have long since braked the moon's spin to the point where she cannot turn independently. The astronomers calculate that this taming of the moon was accomplished so gradually that each million years made scarcely any difference, only the accumulated billions having a really dramatic effect. Yet even now while the moon's dry face is anchored by gravity to the earth, and the earth still turns and turns but more and more slowly, we can sense, abstractly through mathematics, the slight changes in the balancing forces that are almost unbelievably delicate but are still steadily pushing the moon and proportionately lengthening the month. According to Darwin's reckoning, the moon must stop going away when the month reaches 55 of our present days in length, for by then (assuming man has not tampered with it) the earth's rotation will have slowed down so much that the day will also be as long as 55 present days. In other words, the earth too will hold one face toward the moon as both bodies slowly circle each other like tired dancers, and with the moon standing still in the sky our lunar tides will cease to flow or to push the moon any further.

The date for this remote event has been tentatively set by various astronomers as somewhen between the years A.D. 10,000-000,000 and 50,000,000,000, and the moon is approaching it now by receding from us at the dainty pace of only three fifths of an inch a year. If you have trouble believing that anyone could compute a fraction of an inch of annual shift 240,000 miles away, remember that it is average motion over a long period of time and that the moment the moon's edge blocks out a star can be measured with great precision, allowance being made for the exact altitude of whatever lunar slope or valley actually snips off that tiny beam of light. When you use equations involving both time and space, exact determination of the time factors enables you to solve for the space factors with comparable exactitude.

Then sometime before the dry summer of the year A.D. 50,000-000,000, the spinning of the earth may be so slowed down by the remaining solar tides that the day will begin to be longer even than the elongated month of that scarce-imaginable time — the same earthly day that is now lengthening to the merry tune of a thousandth of a second every century — and the lunar tides will gradually begin again, this time in the reverse direction as the moon rises in the west and sets in the east, and will pull Earth and moon together instead of pushing them apart — something you may understand abstractly (if you've ever studied physics) as an inevitable consequence of the "law of conservation of angular momentum."

Thus, almost imperceptibly, if moon and Earth should still exist in such an inconceivably remote age, the moon may begin its long journey back to the earth again. And thus at last the stretch from sunrise to sunset will literally approach a coon's age and each night become an occasion for hibernating. Whatever intelligent beings remain on Earth then will be able to live in daylight, or darkness or twilight as long as they choose just by moving occasionally in the appropriate direction. Women (if evolution has preserved them) may actually be able to order a time of day to fit a mood or a dress instead of having to adapt themselves to the daily schedule as we do now.

If all this (which is based on but one of many theories) seems a mite strange, consider Mars, whose moons are so fast they can be read almost as easily as the hands of a clock. The Martian day already is three times as long as his inner month as defined by his nearer moon, Phobos, which thrice rises in the west and zips across to set in the east before Mars can rotate once. Meanwhile, the Martian outer month (four times longer) lasts so little more than his day that his midget farther moon, Deimos (5 miles in diameter), hangs above the horizon for more than two of its months (61 earthly hours) and passes through all its phases twice between rising and setting.

No one seems to have calculated just when our moon will

come home to roost, but it will definitely be long after the cows come home, if ever, and the manner of such coming has been worked out considerably — a dramatic show indeed, this spectacle that's in store for our descendants — all provided, of course, that we have any and that the sun is still burning then and that the earth and moon have been left to their natural courses.

It is hard to describe such a tremendous thing as the moon's descent with factual realism. How will she make the landing? Will the earth and moon first face each other fixedly while the round moon slowly settles upon one spot? Could we choose the spot — say, our largest ocean (if we still have any ocean) — and direct the moon there? Would our oceans and atmosphere (if atmosphere remains) be partially sucked up by the moon and flow all around it and around the contact place, leaving our old seas half dry and new continents exposed? Or would the moon come spiraling in at speed and land slantwise on the equator to roll around the earth many times before coming to rest? Would any of us have a chance to survive the terrific earthquakes and transcontinental tidal waves and unimaginable hurricanes, the thunderous tornadoes, the black dust storms thousands of miles deep? Which way will be up when the moon roosts on the earth, and what sort of life will be possible to any survivors?

The actual event, as forecast by modern astrophysical knowledge, finesses many of these fearful questions in a surprising manner. The first thing that will be noticed, say astronomers, is that the approaching moon will have developed a protrusion toward the earth. Viewed from space, the moon will be growing more and more egg-shaped, an invariable trait among large nonspinning secondary bodies which get close to their primaries. And the small end of the egg will always aim at the earth, ever reaching out nearer and nearer under the eternal "come hither" of gravity.

The moon is even today slightly eggy. She is, after all, a

large nonspinning secondary, and her paunch aimed toward us has been measured as 3,000 feet higher than the average lunar surface. This is sixteen times as much Earth tide as the moon should have at 240,000 miles, and astronomers explain it as a "fossil tide" that froze that way when her distance was only 90,000 miles. But by A.D. 100,000,000,000 or so the reapproaching moon may be literally as ovoid as a hen's egg. And as gravity eggs her on still nearer (to about 5,000 miles' distance), astronomers say she will inevitably crack and great rifts will open up her interior and she will rapidly separate into two, then three, four, and more pieces, each of which will tend to disintegrate further as it continues to circle around the earth.

The fundamental reason for this is that at about 5,000 miles the gravity of the earth must begin to affect the moon's material more than the moon's own gravity does, so the material will spontaneously fall away from the moon system to form itself into a new equilibrium in more intimate partnership with the earth. The experts do not agree on exactly how successive steps of this extraordinary process will take place, but they are largely united in their opinion that such a break-up is a natural development, one which, under critical circumstances of satellite proximity, must happen. In fact, they can see it happening in our own solar system right now. Not every stage of it, of course, is visible in this twentieth-century instant of slow astronomical time, but the inmost moons of Jupiter, Saturn and Neptune are deduced to be egg-shaped and headed for the break-up point, while Mars' fast moon, Phobos, is so ripe it could pop almost any millennium now. Indeed, Phobos circles so close above the Martian equator that, like a fat man's middle button, it cannot be seen from either pole. On the other hand, the rings of Saturn are believed to be the strewn debris of a moon that has already broken apart and become pulverized — this fairly recently, astronomically speaking, in fact perhaps during the hundred million years just past.

One tends to think of moons as rigid spheres like stone cannonballs, for most known moons seem to be made of stone or solid material of comparable mass. Yet a stone as big as a moon behaves in many ways more like a liquid than a solid. Not only does any solid body larger than 60 miles in diameter melt in its center in about a billion years, according to astronomer Gerard P. Kuiper of Yerkes Observatory, but even the unmolten outer parts have elastic qualities and flow under the influence of gravity, gradually assuming whatever shape conforms to the net dictates of equilibrium. Just as a compact bucketful of water emptied out a tower window quickly turns into rain, so there is a definite range of nearness to its planet through which a moon cannot pass without disintegrating — without becoming, in a manner of speaking, unmoonly. This range, discovered in 1850 by Edouard Roche, a French mathematician, is called Roche's limit. For a satellite of the same density as its planet, the disintegration distance has been calculated at 2.44 times the planet's radius between the two centers. Saturn's rings, for example, are wholly within Roche's limit, while all known moons of all planets remain outside, including even Phobos by the slim margin of 660 miles. In fact no exception to the law has yet been observed anywhere.

So the astronomers can judge with considerable confidence the life expectancy of any settling moon as it spirals closer and closer to its planetary disintegration zone until the strain of its paunch tide becomes unbearable and it snaps in two — like a rubber band. Such a forecast, far from guesswork, is the result of careful calculation. The elasticity of stone and other materials in astronomical masses has indeed been figured out closely enough to give a table of the break-up radii for different substances. A gaseous moon, for instance, comes apart where a liquid satellite would be safe, and a molten moon, moving farther in, must burst where a solid moon need never fear to tread.

Although Phobos' ten-mile diameter may be too small to give it a Roche's limit outside Mars' atmosphere, all the larger moons seem destined for eventual disintegration, whereupon all of their pieces that don't somehow fall into the planet must continue on their orbits, distorting themselves eggwise, bursting again and again from tidal stress till they become small enough to lose their elasticity, when probably only the friction of occasional collisions will continue to wear them down from boulders to stones to gravel to sand to dust as they revolve endlessly around the sky. Thus we should expect one day to witness the great rings of Jupiter!

Eventually Uranus and Neptune will sprout rings the same way when their inner moons break up. And almost exactly the same thing is bound to happen to the earth if celestial nature is left to its own devices long enough. Gerard Kuiper, authority on the solar system, thinks the earth has got rid of one such "sediment ring" already, mostly by having our newborn moon plow through it on her way out toward her present orbit. In any case, the accompanying shower of huge chunks and moony meteorites could be terrifying, not to say devastating, if not countered in some way. But somehow I don't think the problem need be depressing to an enterprising species like us with billions of years to plan in.

A key to ultimate moon undoing, of course, is tidal action, so it is helpful to look at the tides if we are to understand the fullness of moon history, past or future. The ancient Arabs made a beginning when they deduced that tides were caused by the expansion and contraction of the sea under the heat of moonlight, while the Chinese thought of the ocean as the earth's actual blood that was pumped rhythmically by some yet undiscovered terrestrial heart.

Only in modern times have we learned that all tides result from the fact that the gravitational pull on the near side of a body is stronger than the pull on its far side. Thus oceans on Earth become distorted as parts nearest the moon (and, to a lesser degree, the sun) pull away from the less responsive solid earth, while the solid earth in turn pulls away from the still less respectful sea on its far side. This difference in moon influence between the two sides of the earth now amounts to 7 percent,

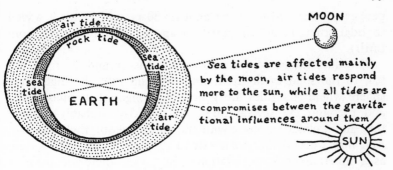

Sea tides are affected mainly by the moon, air tides respond more to the sun, while all tides are compromises between the gravitational influences around them

and in the case of the distant sun to about 2 percent. Ocean tides on Earth, however, are not as simple as they would be if just the moon and sun thus influenced them, for in practice near-by mountains also have a ponderable effect and sea-bottom friction and wind rubbing and coastal contours all exert various lags which, in view of irregular natural oceanic rhythms and the moon's own meandering orbit, make such complications that tide tables are of different "establishment" in every port.

In Tahiti and parts of the Irish coast, for instance, sun tides are stronger than moon tides. In many places, there are four tides a day; in others (called amphodromic points), virtually none. In still others, the morning and evening tides are of very unequal size, or they lag many hours behind the lunar transit.

The tide at A is greater than at B because tides rotate somewhat in latitude as well as in longitude

MOON

Almost everywhere high tides increase with the full or new moon (when the sun adds 30 percent to the moon's pull) or wane to neap strength at the quarters (when the sun's effect cancels 30 percent of the moon's pull). And when the moon is at perigee (closest to the earth) another 30 percent factor is added to tidal strength, as compared to apogee (point farthest from earth).

The tides extend to the water under the ground far from the sea, to the solid earth itself, and even up into the high iono-sphere where sun tides are generally stronger than moon tides and rise and fall several miles twice a day probably because they are in closer harmony with the natural elastic rhythm of air. And now we find that tides extend throughout the solar system as a function of its gravitational field, that there are majestic galactic tides of stars and space dust surging through the Milky Way, and probable supergalactic tides between the remotest and largest organizations of galaxies.

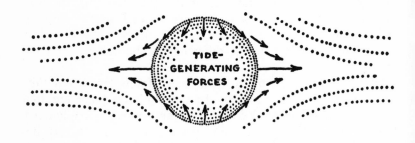

Among the earliest of moon prophets, I have heard, were the ancient Chaldeans, who may have discovered the mystic eclipse interval called the Saros, the regular period of 18 years and 11⅓ days between similar crossings of the sun by the moon, which (some historians think) enabled them to predict eclipses. But most people of their time still considered eclipses the warnings of moody gods and when, as happened to Nicias' Greek army at Syracuse, Sicily, on August 27, 413 B.C., "the sun perished out of the sky," they sometimes disregarded urgent expediency in order to appease the celestial powers, only to get attacked and wiped out by a less scrupulous enemy.

Even the Egyptians did not suspect the complicated irregularities of the eclipse pattern that, we now know, leapfrogs around the earth in spirals, Saros by Saros, working from the poles to the equator every 1,200 years. Nor did the astronomers of the seventeenth century who tried to pin down the moon's schedule with impartial accuracy see any clear path out of their growing confusion. The "synodic month" (period required for the moon to return to its same position in relation to the sun) came out as 29 ½ days, while the "sidereal month" (period of her return in relation to the stars) turned out to be only 27 ⅓ days and the "draconitic month" (period in relation to her nodes) 27 ⅕ days. It was not easy to decide which was the proper month nor how any of them should be fitted into the year.

The movement of the moon, in fact, proved even harder to keep track of than the gyrations of the planets, traditionally known as the "wandering stars," because its relative nearness to Earth made its apparent motion (including its seeming irregularity) many times greater. And such details as precession and the discrepancy between axis of turning and axis of symmetry taxed the genius of Newton, inventor of the calculus, so heavily he once admitted that his "head never ached except when studying lunar theory." Even as recently as thirty-five years ago when E. W. Brown of Yale completed his great work on the orbit of the moon, which stands today (despite our new age of electronic calculating machines) as a culminating achievement of mathematical astronomy, the scientific world gaped to realize he had spent a quarter of a century devising, correcting, checking and polishing a single equation for the moon's motion that covers some 250 large pages!

A simpler way of looking at the moon's inextricable behavior is to analogize her intimate relationship with the earth as a kind of dependency between a mother and grown daughter who live together. For not only does the moon move about the earth; the earth also moves about the moon. Putting both motions together, Newton found, as he had hoped and expected, that there was a common center of gravity for the combination. It was as if the two were joined by an invisible rod from the

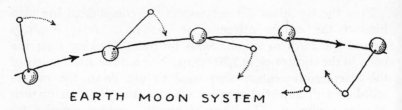

EARTH MOON SYSTEM

center of the earth to the center of the moon, a rod ever twirling
like a baton in the hands of an aloof drum major, the sun,
around whom the common center of gravity (axis of the twirling rod) moves in a smooth ellipse. The marvelous perfection
of this system has been remarked by many great thinkers from
Kepler to Einstein. Exact measurement of the location of the
common center of gravity (about 3,000 miles moonward from
the center of the earth yet still 1,000 miles below our land and
sea) has enabled us to "weigh the moon" after filling in
Newton's basic equation with the gravitational constant. As
the distance of the centers of the two bodies (from the common
center of gravity) is inversely proportional to their masses, and the
common center is about $\frac{1}{82}$ of the way from the earth's center
to the moon's, the moon can weigh only $\frac{1}{82}$ as much as the earth,
or a mere 81,000,000,000,000,000,000 tons.

From this follows the deduction that the moon's specific gravity
is 3.3, that she is made of much lighter stuff than the earth with
its interior of olivine and iron, that she may well be of just ordinary
granite all the way through. But if our moon is lighter than Earth,
she is of much sterner material than some moons like Jupiter's
Callisto, the biggest of all known moons, who, with specific gravity
only 0.6, is literally buoyant enough to float on a watery ocean.

All things considered, ours is far from an average or common
moon. Not only is she the nearest to the sun of all the thirty-two
known moons, but she is much the largest in proportion to her

mother planet. Some astronomers even consider the earth-moon combination a double planet. No other such partnership is to be found in all the solar system, perhaps because, as one theory suggests, satellites that exceed about one fiftieth the mass of their primary tend toward instability and do not long survive.

In any case, there are only five moons bigger than ours in the solar family (Jupiter's Io, Ganymede and Callisto — all named after Jupiter's illicit loves — Saturn's Titan and Neptune's Triton), and none of these is as heavy as one thousandth the weight of its planet. Most of the others are less than a millionth of their primaries, though in other respects they vary to a surprising degree. Mars' little Deimos, for instance, which is smaller than Mount Everest, has such weak gravity that, according to Fred Whipple of Harvard Observatory, a man on it "would weigh only a few ounces and would be capable of jumping several miles, if not completely off the satellite." Mars' west-rising moon, Phobos, might seem to nonmathematical Martians a withershins moon, moving "against the sun" in accord with the definition of that Scottish adjective. But Phobos is really not contrary but just over-eager in an orthodox direction since he revolves to the east even faster than Mars turns eastward behind him.

We have almost everything somewhere in our solar system, however, including several truly contrary moons that move opposite to the spin of their planets. The first of these was discovered in 1898 and named Phoebe. It is Saturn's most remote moon, moving in a retrograde orbit of eight-million-mile radius and counter to Saturn's nine known inner moons, to her rings and to herself! Later, a large satellite called Triton was observed going withershins around Neptune. And four small retrograde moons have been found moving contrariwise about Jupiter, tiny rebels who seem to be thumbing their noses at nature in general. But although at first all of these renegades appear to defy the harmonic order of creation, making a law unto themselves, astronomers believe that at least the Jovian ones are likely to be former asteroids that overtook the big planet from inner (solar) orbits and were thus caught going against the main traffic in a gravitational field that was too much for them. Once captured, they have just not been able to get away, though evidence of their struggle remains visible in most cases in their wild orbits, which form a kind of permanent celestial record analogous to the rings of trees. This sort of record is probably at least as eloquent and durable as any history written in the rock strata of Earth and may even be comparable in principle to human memory stored in patterns of atomic orbits in the brain.

We are by no means, however, at the end of the amazing variety among our known moons. One of Jupiter's is three-quarters frozen water by volume, which practically makes it a snowball. Another Jovite that appears as faint as a candle three thousand miles away got lost for thirteen years on its eccentric orbit and had to be rediscovered by electronic computer at a range of 500 million miles. Saturn's Titan, which is approximately twice as big as our own, is the only moon in the whole solar system known to have an atmosphere. Although the titanic "air" is far from the humanly breathable kind we are used to and is certainly very cold, it just conceivably could support some sort of life.

And the oddest moon of all may be Saturn's piebald ninth satellite, Iapetus — this one less than half the size of ours and, like it, holding one face always toward its planet. Yet as Iapetus moves around Saturn, its brightness varies by a factor of five, showing that one side is five times as light in shade as the other and presumably smoother in texture by a like amount. One can speculate that Iapetus may have been disfigured on one side by some great explosion on Saturn, or perhaps it happened at the time of the creation of the rings, or in some collision with another moon or asteroid or comet. Or could Iapetus be just a lopsided piece of some earlier moon? Or possibly the result of a billion years of eclipse erosion — erosion on one face only through abrupt temperature drops during eclipses?

One does not hear any talk about submoons in modern observatories but I cannot help but wonder whether there may be a few submoons about too — tiny natural satellites of satellites some-where in our system. None has yet been discovered. But that does not prove their nonexistence. Since most moons themselves have been hard to find and Jupiter's outer moons could not be seen with the naked eye even from Jupiter, submoons would naturally be almost impossible to detect — even in the systems of the nearest planets. The bigger moons of the giant planets would be the most likely hosts of submoons, of course, though a submoon (probably a small fraction of a mile in diameter) would be invisible even to the 200-inch reflecting telescope at this great distance. Our own moon, on the other hand, could hardly have any submoons much larger than a meteor without their being detected by now, for her first artificial submoon (the Russian rocket that photographed her back side) is definitely within the realm of detectability.

Another trait of moons that has long fascinated me is their tend-ency to rock back and forth, and I used to think that when our own moon finally settled one face toward the earth it might have reached equilibrium like a well-oiled but slightly uneven wheel spinning on a shaft, at last ceasing its full rotation to rock pon-derously like a dying pendulum to and fro over millions of years. But astrophysicists say there is too much tidal viscosity for that. In effect, the moon's oil contains a soupçon of glue. And the only rocking it can do is the 12 ° of arc it is now seen to swing through each month, showing us one cheek at first quarter, another at the third. This so-called libration is caused by the fact that, although the moon rotates (on its own axis) at the same average rate that it revolves (around the earth), the *even*ness of the *rotation* is not quite matched by the *uneven*ness of the *revolution*, which, being elliptical rather than circular, speeds up at perigee, slows down at apogee, rocking earthwise to the rhythm of a particular kind of slow lunar lullaby known only to the boundless cradle of the sky.

That there are more than moons to occupy the astronomers these nights seems evident from the strange fact that eight of Jupiter's moons, discovered over the past two thirds of a century, have not even yet been named. And as I float through my bottom-less garden of stars and watch our own solitary moon swinging slowly onward, I ponder the significance of such pointed neglect.

MOON TABLE

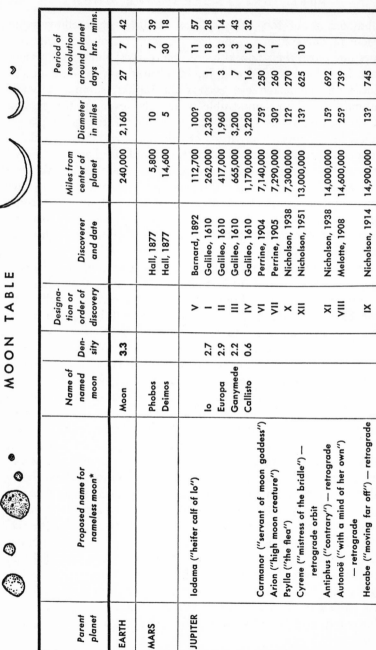

Parent planet	Proposed name for nameless moon*	Name of named moon	Density	Designation or order of discovery	Discoverer and date	Miles from center of planet	Diameter in miles	Period of revolution around planet		
								days	hrs.	mins.
EARTH		Moon	3.3			240,000	2,160	27	7	42
MARS		Phobos			Hall, 1877	5,800	10		7	39
		Deimos			Hall, 1877	14,600	5		30	18
JUPITER	Iodama ("heifer calf of Io")			V	Barnard, 1892	112,700	100?		11	57
		Io	2.7	I	Galileo, 1610	262,000	2,320	1	18	28
		Europa	2.9	II	Galileo, 1610	417,000	1,960	3	13	14
		Ganymede	2.2	III	Galileo, 1610	665,000	3,200	7	3	43
		Callisto	0.6	IV	Galileo, 1610	1,170,000	3,220	16	16	32
	Carmanor ("servant of moon goddess")			VI	Perrine, 1904	7,140,000	75?	250	17	
	Arion ("high moon creature")			VII	Perrine, 1905	7,290,000	30?	260	1	
	Psylla ("the flea")			X	Nicholson, 1938	7,300,000	12?	270		
	Cyrene ("mistress of the bridle") — retrograde orbit			XII	Nicholson, 1951	13,000,000	13?	625	10	
	Antiphus ("contrary") — retrograde			XI	Nicholson, 1938	14,000,000	15?	692		
	Autonoë ("with a mind of her own") — retrograde			VIII	Melotte, 1908	14,600,000	25?	739		
	Hecabe ("moving far off") — retrograde			IX	Nicholson, 1914	14,900,000	13?	745		

(Moon Table continued)

Parent planet	Direction of orbit	Name of named moon	Density	Designation or order of discovery	Discoverer and date	Miles from center of planet	Diameter in miles	Period of revolution around planet days	hrs.	mins.
SATURN	normal	Janus		X	Dollfus, 1966	90,000	150?		18	37
	normal	Mimas	0.5	VII	Herschel, 1789	115,300	270?		22	53
	normal	Enceladus		VI	Herschel, 1789	148,000	300?	1	8	18
	normal	Tethys		V	Cassini, 1684	183,000	700?	1	21	18
	normal	Dione		IV	Cassini, 1684	235,000	650?	2	17	41
	normal	Rhea		II	Cassini, 1672	327,600	1,000?	4	12	25
	normal	Titan	3.5	I	Huygens, 1655	760,000	2,850?	15	22	41
	normal	Hyperion		VIII	Bond, 1848	920,000	250?	21	6	38
	normal	Iapetus		III	Cassini, 1671	2,212,000	800?	79	7	56
	retrograde	Phoebe		IX	Pickering, 1898	8,040,000	200?	550	10	
URANUS	slightly retrograde	Miranda		V	Kuiper, 1948	81,000	100?	1	9	55
	slightly retrograde	Ariel		I	Lassell, 1851	119,000	300?	2	12	29
	slightly retrograde	Umbriel		II	Lassell, 1851	166,000	250?	4	3	28
	slightly retrograde	Titania		III	Herschel, 1787	272,000	600?	8	16	56
	slightly retrograde	Oberon		IV	Herschel, 1787	365,000	550?	13	11	7
NEPTUNE	retrograde	Triton		I	Lassell, 1846	220,000	2,600?	5	21	3
	normal	Nereid		II	Kuiper, 1949	3,350,000	200?	359	10	

* Of these proposed names, Seth Nicholson, discoverer of four Jovian moons, writes the author: "The names you suggest . . . are good logical ones." But skeptically, he adds, "I think that, like Pullman cars, they will be known by their numbers, not their names."

I scrutinize my moon table (q.v.) and dream a little and meditate and muse on names for nameless worlds.

It may be just my own private form of lunacy in this trackless void, but I can't help but wonder how long such celestial pathos must continue — how long will neglected satellites go mooning onward in their lonely dudgeon — how long can the tentmaker's son go unheeded:

> Yon rising moon that looks for us again—
>   How oft hereafter will she wax and wane;
> How oft hereafter rising look for us
>   Through this same garden — and for one in vain!

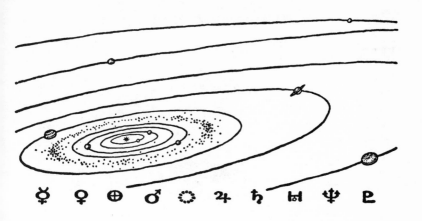

$$\text{☿ ♀ ⊕ ♂ ○ ♃ ♄ ♅ ♆ ♇}$$

4. OUR SISTER PLANETS

I FIND IT RATHER HARD TO REMEMBER, out here in pathless space, just how those mystic, sibling worlds called Venus, Mars, Jupiter and Saturn appeared from Earth. And even harder is it to recover much perspective on how they seemed in ancient times — say, in the dim dawn days of Greece when Anaximandros of Miletos expatiated upon creation in the sixth century B.C., opining (I've read) that "something capable of begetting hot and cold out of the unbounded was separated off at the origin of the world. And from this arose a sphere of flame encasing the earth as the bark around a tree. When this had been further compassed by certain rings, the sun, moon and stars were born." As for the earth itself, he went on, it "swings free, held in its place by nothing. It is fixed by its equal distance from everything. We are on one of the surfaces, and the other is on the opposite side."

Half a century later, Pythagoras of Samos, who has been called the patron saint of science, intuitively divided creation at the level of the moon into a *super*lunar sphere, containing all the regular stars, all ascended souls and immortal gods, and a *sub*lunar sphere, where dwelt all bodies that could be classed as irregular, mortal or dead. He was the most influential western philosopher of his time, and his appointment of the moon's range as the borderline between regularity and irregularity, arbitrary though it now appears, carried great weight. The wandering stars, called planets (from *planētēs*, a vagabond), were already understood to be higher than the moon, which made them superlunar and eternal — and this raised the difficult question of why they did not move with more regularity. Their confusing movements had even been compared by Anaximenes (also of Miletos) to "the gyrations of leaves falling off the tree of stars." Yet Pythagoras resolved the dilemma with his profound and contagious faith in divine order expressed in a law of universal harmony under which the planets would be found to revolve in circles upon invisible spheres if only one could measure them in true perspective.

Pythagoras is said to have played the phorminx, a seven-stringed

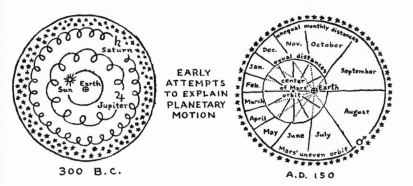

EARLY
ATTEMPTS
TO EXPLAIN
PLANETARY
MOTION

300 B.C.

A.D. 150

harp made of tortoiseshell — reputedly invented by Hermes, god of science and eloquence. Instrumental music in those days was generally considered a form of religious ritual, but Pythagoras seems to have been so fascinated with the mystical abstraction of numbers that he experimented mathematically with the harmonics of the vibrating string and became impressed with the remarkable similarity between musical intervals and the spacings of the planets, which then included the wandering sun and moon. For, according to Hippolytos (c. 400 B.C.), "Pythagoras maintained that the universe sings and is constructed in accordance with harmony; and he was the first to reduce the motions of the seven heavenly bodies to rhythm and song."

This is undoubtedly the origin of the music of the spheres in which the seven classical planets symbolized the seven notes of the scale, and the heptachord in turn founded the seven-day week and perhaps the seven vowels of the Greek alphabet upon the same seven spheres. Certainly this is such a reasonable derivation of our common hebdomad that it is hard to imagine how else the entire civilized earth could have accepted the basic septimal rhythm of the calendar with its Sun day, Moon day, Tiw's (Mars') day, Woden's (Mercury's) day, Thor's (Jupiter's) day, Frigg's (Venus') day and Saturn's day.

The Greeks soon seemed unable to imagine any planet without its orbital sphere, upon which it moved in a perfect circle, any other orbit being obviously less than godly. And for them, each of the seven celestial immortals exerted its particular mood upon the temper of the central earth — giving us the corresponding moody adjectives of sunny, looney, martial, mercurial, jovial, venereal and saturnine — while the less-specialized Greek tragedies became *dis-asters* (against the stars), each wanton barbarian raid *ex-orbitant* (out of orbit) and anything beyond the normal four world ingredients of earth, water, air and fire, a *quintessence* (fifth element). And so forth.

Ptolemy of Alexandria later placed an "eight sphere" outside the original seven to hold the fixed stars and the Milky Way, and he and other mathematicians added still more spheres to the celestial scale in efforts to account for all the apparent eccentricities of the planets, including the puzzling but recurrent figure-eight-shaped *hippopede* (horse-fetter) maneuvers of Mars, Jupiter and

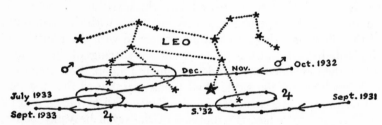

APPARENT TRACKS OF MARS (ABOVE) AND JUPITER (BELOW), MONTH BY MONTH, THROUGH THE CONSTELLATION OF THE LION

Saturn. Out of these spheres developed the famous concept of the epicycle, a small rapid orbit whose center revolves slowly around a larger orbit which may swing in turn about a still larger one, brilliantly explaining the most baffling of planetary motions better than they had ever been explained before. But somehow it seemed forced and unnatural, and successively closer measurements of the planets kept calling for more spheres embellished with more epicycles until, by the sixteenth century, it took more than eighty spheres to account for the observed movements, and even that number did it very imperfectly.

Opposing this lamentable trend toward complexity, a few daring visionaries had conceived of simpler explanations, such as Heraclides of Pontos' rash idea in the fourth century B.C. that "since Venus and Mercury are never observed at any great angular distance from the sun, they may revolve about it" or the even more startling and probably original proposal of Philolaos of Croton a century earlier that "the earth circles around the sun."

Unfortunately, few people had thought of keeping systematic records of the positions of the planets in those days, so there was little evidence for decisively proving or disproving any theory. With the possible exception of a 360-year series of Chaldean star measurements begun under King Nabonassar in 747 B.C., and to a lesser degree the Babylonian and Egyptian efforts, observing had never been regarded as particularly important. Noble concepts of the mind were rated much higher. But the intuition of Heraclides and the inspirations of Philolaos and, later, of the great Aristarchos of Samos (who held that the earth not only revolves around the sun but spins daily on its own axis) seemed more blasphemous than noble — and where was there any solid datum to contradict the obvious fact that the great earth is fixed in the middle of creation while the dainty little stars and parasitic planets swing respectfully around it? How could any devout astrologer take seriously the wild conjectures of such later philosophers as Nicholas of Cusa that the earth cannot be central because the universe is infinite and infinity has no center?

It was not until a German (dwelling in Poland) named Nikolaus Koppernigk, better known by his Latin name of Copernicus, got exasperated at the ridiculous numbers of spheres and epicycles required to patch up the heavens that Philolaos' and Aristarchos' old ideas (which Copernicus had read about) were revived and published in A.D. 1543. I am referring, of course, to Copernicus' famous work *De Revolutionibus Orbium Coelestium,* On the Revolutions of the Celestial Spheres, which included the startling hypothesis (of Ecphantos the Pythagorean, Hicetas of Syracuse, Heraclides and Aristarchos) that the earth rotates daily about its

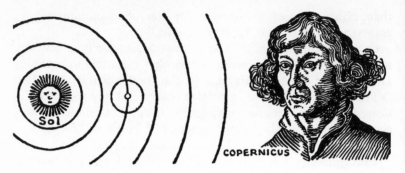

own axis. This idea had been made much more plausible by the recent exploits of Columbus, Balboa and Magellan. But Copernicus could find only fourteen observations to support his argument that the sun is the center of a system of revolving planets, a number that, he admitted, was far too small on which to claim a proof. So his concept was offered mainly on the strength of its simplicity. That seemed reason enough to his orderly mathematical mind, which still saw no need to question the orthodox Pythagorean uniformity of circular orbits in a basic machinery of spheres. Yet almost despite his own efforts, as in the case of his older contemporary, Columbus, Copernicus opened up a world so unbelievable that he himself did not live to recognize it.

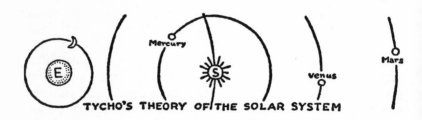

TYCHO'S THEORY OF THE SOLAR SYSTEM

Strangely enough, the complete acceptance of Copernicus' new celestial order was to come in large measure from a colorful and arrogant Danish nobleman named Tycho Brahe, who not only did not believe in much of it but supposed he had practically disproved it because his pre-eminent instruments could not detect sidereal parallax, or the difference in apparent direction of a body (say, the North Star) as seen from different places (say, opposite sides of the earth's orbit). He insisted, quite reasonably, that at least a slight bit of parallax must be revealed if the earth were really swinging around the sun — for, in those days before the telescope, no man had ever heard or dreamed of such a fantastic thing as the since proven distance of the nearest star at 25,000,000-000,000 miles.

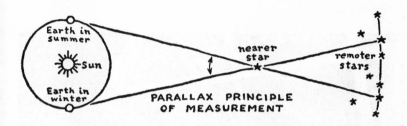

Tycho Brahe was different from the usual playboy son of an aristocrat. Although he lost his nose in a duel at twenty and wore a gold replacement the rest of his life, he was such a serious student of astronomy, reverently putting on his finest robes to measure and honor the stars, that King Frederick II of Denmark presented him with the island of Hveen near Copenhagen and financed the erection there of the fabulous Uraniborg ("Castle of the Heavens"), complete with printing press, paper mill and running water, where Tycho and his staff made systematic observations of stars and planets for more than twenty years. Indeed, Tycho is considered the first modern scientist in that he not only built instruments of remarkable accuracy, including a quadrant 37 feet high calibrated to the minute of arc and a clepsydra which kept time through a steady dripping of mercury, but he repeated every measurement four times, made precise allowance for the errors of all his equipment and even worked out a refraction table to correct altitude angles for the bending of light rays that had passed through the thick lower air. Using as many as nine assistants at one time, he insisted that every fact be checked and rechecked before it was recorded with unprecedented and scrupulous care. A clue to the quality of his results is his successful measurement of the length of the year to within a second of the modern figure, and construction of a five-foot globe of brass to represent the sky on which he engraved the positions of 777 stars and planets so exactly that they and his paper records later formed the main basis of Kepler's discoveries and, to only a slightly lesser degree, made possible Newton's great work on the laws of gravity and motion, which has been the plinth of science and engineering ever since.

Johannes Kepler, the thirty-year-old German assistant who succeeded Tycho after his death in Prague in 1601, was almost exactly opposite him in temperament. Poor, gentle, sickly and weak in eyesight, he had little stomach for monotonous nightly observations but preferred searching for some clear law in the bewildering whirl of moody planetary motions. That he was meticulous in the popular horoscope service he ran in his spare time is suggested by his calculation of his own conception as having occurred on "16 May, A.D. 1571, at 4:37 a.m.," followed by "a pregnancy lasting 224 days, 9 hours and 53 minutes." That he was a mathematician to the heart is shown by his very logical and successful method of finding an optimum wife by classifying all the ladies of his acquaintance in the order of their eligibility, then proposing down the list to ensure that the first who said "Ja" was automatically the best obtainable.

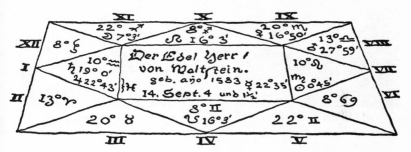

WALLENSTEIN'S HOROSCOPE CAST BY KEPLER • 1608

Although he enthusiastically accepted the Copernican theory for its convincing simplicity, Kepler was so steeped in astrology and mysticism that he was a virtual Pythagorean and never ceased looking for harmonies or unsuspected relationships between the motions of the several planets. Why were there exactly six planets, now counting the earth but not the sun or moon? Was it because six was a "perfect" number, the product as well as the sum of one, two and three?

One of Kepler's most serious projects was circumscribing the "sphere" of each planetary orbit with a different one of the five regular solids (tetrahedron, cube, octahedron, dodecahedron and icosahedron) to see if they would exactly fit between the spherical surfaces as he devoutly presumed they should if the heavens were really divine. The fits, however, turned out to be only "fairly good" — definitely not perfect — so Kepler turned to music as the mathematical function that might yield a better clue to planetary intervals. He actually transcribed the music of the spheres, evidently having accepted the tradition that each planet was alive and be-

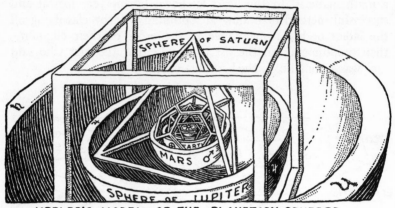

KEPLER'S MODEL OF THE PLANETARY SPHERES

souled if not presided over by its individual guardian angel who alone could hear its harmony. He was so poor at this time that he must have wondered whether his own terrestrial angel was really listening but, transposing from relative velocities in various parts of their different orbits, he somehow came up with basic melodies for each planet, the earth's notes being simply "mi, fa, mi" repeated over and over, which could be interpreted as "miseria, famina, miseria" — misery, famine, and more misery — the prevailing doleful theme of Earth. Little Mercury's tone was soprano, Venus' appropriately contralto and, continuing outward from the sun, Mars' a falsetto tenor and the voices of the giants Jupiter and Saturn both deeply bass.

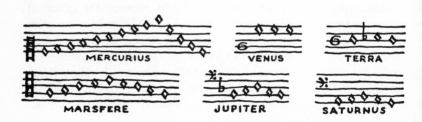

Yet always the beautiful abstractions of mathematics nourished the exuberant patterns of Kepler's reasoning. In an age when almost no one believed in the reign of law in nature, he had faith in ultimate divine justice, which meant order, which meant law. And no matter how deep his frustration, he kept on trying and rejecting, plotting and measuring, one after another the geometric forms and combinations that might explain the weird motions of Mars so painstakingly pinpointed by old Tycho — Mars, who seemed to offer a particular challenge with his apparent "horse-fetter" gyrations whenever he passed close to the earth — Mars, whose distance away (therefore his position in space) could not be seen, but only his direction from an earth which was itself moving in an invisible, unknown manner around the sun.

Reluctantly Kepler soon had to abandon the circle as the divine orbital shape. Even with the help of elaborate epicycles, it just could not be made to fit reality any closer than eight minutes, about one seventh of a degree. Though another astronomer suggested that a discrepancy of only 8′ of arc might easily have resulted from a slip in a planetary observation without the aid of a telescope, Kepler firmly replied that it was "quite out of the question for Tycho to have made an error of that magnitude." After he had also rejected the egg-shaped orbit and was anxiously but carefully plotting out all the other forms of the oval he could think of, Kepler suddenly discovered to his unbounded delight that the simple ellipse with its off-center foci (originally rejected as ungodly) was what he was looking for. Perhaps only then did he remember Tycho's careful description of a comet's elliptical orbit in 1588, the first such ever known!

At any rate, Kepler could almost feel Tycho's proud smile of

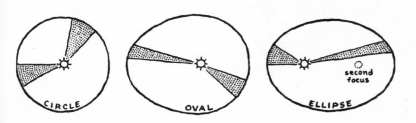

admiration when, in 1609, a few months before Galileo Galilei in Padua built the first astronomical telescope, he started writing out his three great laws of planetary motion: (1) *The orbit of every planet is an ellipse with the sun at one focus.* Which stands to this day a pillar of celestial mechanics.

With the orbital shape thus at last cleared up, it was relatively easy to define the manner of planetary movement, irrevocably uniting time with space: (2) *The straight line joining a planet and the sun sweeps over equal areas during equal times.*

And finally, after another nine years of hard struggle to tune in more closely to the elusive music, he noticed a striking similarity in the last two columns (below) of one of his many tables of periods and distances

PLANET	RELATIVE DISTANCE FROM SUN	PERIOD IN YEARS	SQUARE OF THE PERIOD	CUBE OF THE DISTANCE
MERCURY	0.387	0.241	0.058	0.058
VENUS	0.723	0.615	0.378	0.378
EARTH	1	1	1	1
MARS	1.524	1.881	3.538	3.540
JUPITER	5.203	11.862	140.707	140.851
SATURN	9.539	29.458	867.774	867.977

from which he immediately derived his now famous harmonic law: (3) *The squares of the periods of revolution of the planets are proportional to the cubes of their respective mean distances from the sun.*

If all this seems fairly simple now that we have been shown

the way, remember that Kepler was the first man in world history able to define the actual movement of the spheres. And if he had lived beyond the age of fifty-nine he very well might have found the answer to his final quest for a unifying principle to explain his by then famous triad of laws — something which it took no less a genius than Isaac Newton, the great English mathematician, to accomplish half a century later with his epochal definition of gravitation: *Every particle of matter in the universe attracts every other particle with a force proportional to the product of their masses and varying inversely as the square of the distance between their centers.*

We will meet Newton again in the second part of this book. Here we are dealing with those sisters of Earth, the planets, which were Kepler's particular concern as the most challenging celestial beings of his day. And their fascination for modern astronomers in their variety and alien mystery is not likely to diminish while they draw rapidly closer to our reach.

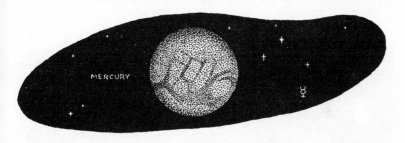

Mercury, nearest planet to the sun, is also the swiftest and smallest — in fact, smaller even than Ganymede and Callisto, Jupiter's largest moons. Although the Greeks named him Mercury when they saw him setting just after sunset, some of them also called him Apollo when he rose at dawn, even though the better educated among them were well aware that he was one and the same. Probably the name Mercury finally stuck because of his mercurial temperament as expressed in his fickle elusiveness. His year is only 88 Earth days, and he spends them moving at speeds ranging from 23 to 36 miles a second, swooping now within 29 million miles of the sun, now way out to 44 million miles. This eccentric orbit makes him invisible most of the time, yet early in this century it provided one of the important proofs of Einstein's theory of general relativity, as we shall later see.

Although it was long believed that Mercury, like our moon, always kept only one face toward his primary (the sun), astronomers using doppler radar in 1965 discovered that he actually rotates on his own axis in about 59 Earth days, or a third faster than he revolves around the sun. But because he circles the sun every 88 Earth days, his own day works out to some 180 Earth days which, curiously enough, means that he has a day twice as long as his year. That is about all we yet know of Mercury who is forever ducking shyly out of sight in the sun's glare, and at best is far from an inviting destination for an exploratory voyage. His sunny side is hot enough (770° F.) to melt lead and tin and has long since cooked his atmosphere completely away. Even his shifting three-week-long seasons cannot much atone for the climatic extremes of his lit and unlit iron mountains.

as the evening star   VENUS AS SEEN FROM EARTH   as the morning star   ♀

Venus, the second planet from the sun and twin sister of the earth, offers a gracious contrast. And, I'm glad to say, much more hospitality, even if, as befits her name, she is well shrouded in feminine mystery. Her veil is not just a figure of speech either, for the obvious brightness of Venus does not come from anything so firm as flesh but rather from her flowing sari of white clouds.

Like Mercury, Venus is a moonless planet who, swinging regularly between us and the sun, has lunelike phases of her own. Thus we have known her shady side ever since Galileo first caught her in his glass and saw that she must circle completely around the sun — strong evidence in support of Copernicus. And we have recorded her extraordinary changes in appearance from a remote gibbous peach beyond the sun to a close crescent of pale pumpkin six times greater in diameter as she overtakes the earth every nineteenth month on her inside track — these being the first telescopic revelations of the mysterious Hesperus of the evening and Phosphorus of the morning from Greek antiquity.

Her crescent indeed is a unique sight and different from anything else known to the heavens, being not at all the sharp sickle of our young moon's blade but a kind of soft pearly sash encircling more than half her body with the enchanting haziness imparted by a lush atmosphere. And when the sun is almost directly behind her, Venus does not vanish completely like a new moon, for a delicate negligee of filtered light lingers around her silhouette in a complete ring — actually a halo of pure gloaming bestowed by her radiant sire.

Yet for all her dainty charm, Venus stands no less than champion in visual magnitude among all the fixed and wandering stars to be seen from Earth. And when she is at her maximum brilliance, between two and three weeks before and after her synodic rendezvous with the sun, she is easily visible on earth in full daylight and will cast distinct shadows on any clear moonless night.

One is apt to forget, moreover, that since her almost circular orbit never permits her to stray more than 46° in angular distance from the sun, Venus must nearly always be within human sight in the middle of a clear day any time of year — if one but knows exactly where to look. Even though professional navigators traditionally neglect the diurnal Venus, who demands close calculation and usually some patient gazing before one may catch her eye, I sometimes used to call on her for help while flying the lonely Pacific during the Korean airlift — invariably to my advantage and delight. As it was often almost impossible to navigate accurately by the sun alone, when neither moon nor stars were in sight, Venus quite naturally became my second light. Her plotted altitude line thus protected many an unsuspecting high-priority passenger to whom such a clue from Venus at noon would have seemed no more real than a wink from a passing angel — which in sober fact may not be so far from what it was.

As to the question of the kind of world Venus really is underneath her dazzling raiment, it is hard to believe how much the scientists have been able to deduce from small clues. For example, Gerard Kuiper, using filters to exclude all but violet light, took hundreds of pictures that show six vague bands of otherwise invisible "climate" around Venus, comparable to the rainy doldrums, dry horse latitudes and windy jet streams of earth. Radar revealed that Venus has earthlike mountain chains but rotates in a retrograde direction, opposite to the other planets, yet so slowly that she completes only one turn to about 247 of Earth's, which makes her day slightly longer than half her year of 224.7 Earth days. Then came the more intimate clues snooped from a mere 21,648 miles away by the extraordinary flight of man's first successful interplanetary rocket, Mariner II, which sneaked past Venus on December 14, 1962, with sensitive instruments that radioed Earth to tell her her sister planet is surprisingly hot: something like 800° F. all over her fuming surface despite the dense canopy of cool clouds beginning 45 miles above it and reaching to an average level of 60 miles where they are made of ice crystals at —30° F.

Several observers were puzzled by the spectroscopic indication that water vapor is scarce in Venus' clouds (being detectable only in spectrograms made from space), because, they reasoned, a planet so earthlike should logically be expected to have had an origin and history close enough to Earth's to give it a comparable proportion of water along with most of the familiar terrestrial elements. Even the length of Venus' day hints at some sort of ocean tidal action to have braked her rotation so much beyond the gentle terrestrial pace. If there are any watery seas on Venus, however, their vapor should show up strongly in her clouds instead of just the predominating carbon dioxide and faint nitrogen and H_2O lines found in her spectrograms.

Could Venus' natural juices have almost completely evaporated away, as almost surely happened to Mercury? Whatever the answer, the slight disparities in mass and position between Earth and Venus evidently have made a surprising chemical difference. For while Venus' diameter is only 227 miles less than the earth's, her one-sixth smaller mass with its correspondingly reduced gravity has undoubtedly allowed more of her atmosphere to escape — particularly her hydrogen, lightest of all gases and the prime ingredient of water. And as there is no evidence of free oxygen in her atmosphere now, what remains of this vital element has presumably long since consolidated its grip on the planet by combining with various other common elements such as carbon.

Such a hypothesis, at least, would explain the relative abundance of carbon dioxide on Venus. And, interestingly enough it brings up the possibility that our lovely "evening star" may really be the heiress of more than all the fabulous wealth of fairytale and song. For if her oxygen has mostly gone into carbon dioxide, she must have carbon available in tremendous quantities with, very likely, a vast unoxidized residue still remaining in some such natural form as oil or coal. Perhaps, as astronomer Fred Hoyle gaily suggests, the Venusian oceans are literally "oceans of oil" upon a planet "endowed beyond the dreams of the richest Texas oil-king."

Mars, the fourth member of the sun's family and first beyond the earth, is as different from Venus as Venus is different from Mercury. If Venus is Earth's twin sister, Mars is the little brother of both and the most nearly proven abode of life among all the heavenly hosts.

The most unusual thing about Mars from a human viewpoint is his observability, which, oddly enough, is as much due to his small size as to his propitious closeness to Earth at the very periods he appears most "full" with sunlight. For, being smaller than Earth to the degree that a plum is smaller than an orange and of lighter substance, Mars has only a tenth the terrestrial mass and therefore could not retain nearly as much atmospheric shroud despite the astringent effect of a temperature that averages more than 150° F. cooler. Thus the Martian skies are usually free enough of clouds so that we can see his rusty arid plains and bricky deserts, which of course are why Mars looks prevailingly red and why he was named after the bloody god of war.

When telescopic seeing is most nearly perfect, astronomers can pick out even minor details of the suggestive jasperlike landscape: the dark brownish green of his Wedge of Casius, the bright green of Mare Cimmerium, the strong bluish green in Syrtis Major and other spots, the warm coffee color around his dazzling white south polar cap, which is different from the pervading dragon's-blood red of his vast Sahara-like lower latitudes.

The colors change rapidly as the atmospheres of both Earth and Mars shift and filter and refract the passage of light. And large seasonal changes come in the slow Martian year (687 Earth days) when first one pole, then the other, tilts toward the sun, and Mars varies his solar distance by 20 percent, while greeny growth (conceivably lichen) can be seen spreading toward the equator — a "wave of quickening" that astronomer Percival Lowell once measured to move at 2.1 m.p.h. along the Martian "valleys," perhaps spurred by the spring flow in the "canals" bringing "snow water" from the poles to the deserts.

The canal hypothesis, however, was virtually shattered when on July 14, 1965, man's second successful interplanetary rocket, Mariner IV, drifted within 6,118 miles of Mars to take twenty-two close-up photographs which surprised nearly everyone by showing a moonlike landscape of hundreds of craters up to 75 miles across and one-quarter mile deep with hardly a sign of a canal. This practically proved that, despite a little water vapor, it doesn't rain on Mars, for erosion there must be exceedingly slow to have preserved these ancient scars of meteoritic impact (as they are presumed to be), though the fact that they are only one-sixth as numerous as on an equal area of the moon suggests the possibility that Mars once had ample water and a much denser atmosphere, at least during his first 3 billion years. The present blue-green areas can no longer be considered extensive vegetation, however, as chemical tests have found no evidence of chlorophyll there, and the Martian snowcaps and ubiquitous frost seem likely to contain more frozen carbon dioxide than frozen water in view of the now known high CO_2 content of his "air" that is fifty times thinner than Earth's.

While Mars' skies are generally clear, clouds of a probable cirrus type have often been seen there which appear bluish white, transparent and drifting from six to nineteen miles above the ground as measured by their shadows, forming belts roughly parallel to the equator. One giant W-shaped cirrus in 1955 "persisted for a month, evaporating every morning and reforming every afternoon." But occasional denser, yellowish, cumuluslike clouds are seen also, rarely more than two or three miles high and almost surely made of sand or dust. About every fifteen years (1911, 1926, 1941, 1958 . . .), these clouds form into what are probably giant dust storms, sometimes lasting several months and moving with eerie slowness over the Martian deserts, their top speed seldom clocked above four miles an hour. Mars has also a thin stratum of violet haze between the high blue and low yellow clouds which is now generally believed to be composed of carbon dioxide snow crystals.

Thus are revealed in a distant world the three main cloud types of Earth: cirrus, cumulus and stratus. Each is similar to some of our own clouds, yet different and literally unearthly. And they all float higher and slower than their earthly cousins, their loftier altitudes being due to the weaker gravity on Mars, which allows a more gradual pressure decrease with height and thus, strangely, means that above seventeen miles the atmospheric pressure is actually greater on Mars than at the same altitude above Earth.

On the surface, however, as revealed in the surprisingly detailed daily maps that have been made of Martian weather, conditions of both temperature and pressure are remarkably similar to those found about 16 miles above the earth in our stratosphere. This fact is exciting to biologists and philosophers as well as astronomers because it means that, although the Martian atmosphere is thin enough for good observation, it is not necessarily too thin for life. Indeed, for the same reason that a 16-mile-high plateau on Earth (if there were one) would be bound to warm up to a tolerable temperature under direct vertical sun radiation on a windless day, temperatures up to 80° F. have been recorded on Mars' equator shortly after local noon, the Martian day being only 37 minutes longer than the earthly day.

Of course, one should expect any creatures on Mars to be at least as different from the animals of Earth as Earth's animals differ from one another, but there seems to be no reason why there should not be some which have evolved a Martian mode of life on the oxygen, hydrogen, carbon and other elements available there, especially if Mars should turn out to have been warmer and wetter in the critical early stages of his evolution. In fact, the suspected presence of vegetation on Mars, even if only lichen, requires something equivalent to animals to feed on it and create the carbon dioxide essential to most plant life.

Even on Venus, with a surface evidently a lot hotter than boiling water on Earth, there is thought to be a good chance of life in the turbulent middle altitudes of her lush clouds, which, according to Dr. Heinz Haber of the University of California, may include a teeming "biological airsol" of planktonlike microorganisms upon which larger flitting creatures feed — perhaps only to be preyed upon in turn by others still larger and better insulated from the hydrocarbonic surface below.

On cool Mars, of course, there appears to be little to encourage any sort of floating gaseous life, and the need for warmth may instead have driven evolution largely underground. There seems

to be no insurmountable reason why it cannot survive in a shel-
tered environment, however, and the fact that some forms of life
(even on Earth) get along without liquid water or oxygen, plus
the evidence of spectrograms that Mars' thin "air" includes hydrogen compounds like a few produced by terrestrial organisms, has
led astrophysicist Lewis Kaplan of the Jet Propulsion Laboratory
to venture that the clues of Mars "strongly suggest . . . a chemical
environment from which life could evolve."

<hr>

Between Mars and the fifth planet, Jupiter, lies a vast expanse
of sky strewn with nothing much but a few thousand asteroids
or minor planets (to be discussed in detail next chapter), few of
which exceed a dozen miles in diameter. This is an obvious gap
in the order of the spheres that Pythagoras may have sensed
intuitively but which Kepler felt so acutely that he once declared,
"I have become bolder, and now I place a planet between these
two," Mars and Jupiter.

A century and a half later, the continuing absence of Kepler's
"planet" was made all the more conspicuous by Titius of Witten-
berg, who worked out his famous rule of planetary distances that
the German astronomer Johann Elert Bode was later to develop
into the so-called Bode's Law, which gives precise mathematical
expression to the musical intervals of the worlds.

Writing down a series of 4's, one for each planet, Titius and
Bode added to the 4's the numbers 0 for Mercury, 3 for Venus,
6 for Earth, 12 for Mars, 24 for "the missing planet," 48 for Jupiter, and 96 for Saturn, doubling the number for each additional
member. The resultant progression (with its decimal points moved
one place) represented the approximate planetary distances from
the sun in terms of the earth's distance. With the embarassing
exception of Neptune, who eventually had to be replaced by the
recently discovered Pluto, the scheme came remarkably close to
the real distances:

	Bode's Law	Real (average) distance
Mercury	.4	.39
Venus	.7	.72
Earth	1	1
Mars	1.6	1.52
The gap	2.8	2.805
Jupiter	5.2	5.2
Saturn	10	9.54
Uranus	19.6	19.19
Neptune	38.8	30.07
Pluto	77.2	39.52

Whether this curious if limping harmony among our sister spheres could possibly have derived from chance alone is a question that draws by no means as clear a concert of opinions — more light on which will have to await Chapter 6, which touches on the remarkable raising of the sun's family, and Chapter 12, which describes the suggestively similar progression known as Balmer's Ladder in the spectrum.

Nearest and biggest of the four giant planets is Jupiter, who epitomizes in his extravagant behavior all the principal traits of this preponderantly outer and larger faction of the solar tribe. It is appropriate that he was named for the king of the gods, for he is not only a thousand times bigger than the earth but he weighs two and a half times as much as all the other planets put together, being, in a sense, a small unlit star. Yet, since nothing of his actual size or mass could expectably have been known to the ancients and he is almost always exceeded in brilliance by Venus and sometimes by Mars, how they could have divined his greatness is something of a mystery. Was it his relative steadfastness that made the Babylonians call him Nibirru in association with their great god Marduk, whom the Greeks were to call Zeus? Or was it perhaps the subtle combination of his prominence and the dignified independence of his gyrations that elevated him to "Celestial Arbiter of the Happiness of China" in the eleventh century B.C.?

Professors of astronomy like to call Jupiter "the regulator" because his overwhelming gravitational power has probably been a major influence in regulating the orbits of the other planets into approximately a single plane. At any rate, he looks the picture of the inveterate bully: bulging at the waistline, his muscles flabby but flexing mightily, and his dozen janissaries hovering to his beck and nod. Three of his great Galilean moons (of the four discovered by Galileo), in fact, are a good deal bigger than our own, and his family as a whole forms a kind of condensed edition of the solar system, his outer moons taking twice as long to circle him as the earth takes to go around the sun, his double escort of asteroids maintaining ever their same respectful distance for harmonic reasons we will examine in the next chapter, his fickle filiation of three-score comets shuttling feverishly to and fro. On the seemingly mystical subject of harmonics, I might mention the curious fact that the mean daily motion of Io added to twice that of Ganymede always turns out precisely equal to three times the motion of Europa — a relation $(I + 2G = 3E)$ that astronomers describe as "so exact and permanent that all three satellites can never exhibit similar phenomena at the same time."

Through the telescope, Jupiter himself appears a golden disk with many brown, yellow and reddish belts of latitude separated by grayish blue running about his middle. The impression that he is turning so fast he is distorted into the shape of a doorknob is confirmed by measurement of his equatorial diameter, which exceeds his axis by 14 percent. Likewise his actual turning is soon noticed, for, big as he is, he makes a complete revolution every nine hours and fifty minutes, his equator coasting along at 30,000 miles an hour and constantly beset by howling storms that rile his atmosphere to a possible depth of several thousand miles.

If our own equator ever got going anywhere nearly so fast, the earth would surely rupture and newborn moons would burst forth roughshod from where Africa, India and South America now lie lazy in the sun. For someone has figured the ultimate rotational speed limit for each of our revolving planets, a speed reached when the centrifugal force at the equator becomes equal to gravity, and inhabitants, if any, start floating upward into the sky. In the case of Earth, the limiting day (or period of revolution) is 1 hour and 25 minutes — to approach which would be disastrous. Jupiter's limit is 2 hours, 58 minutes, Saturn's 4 hours, 9 minutes, the sun's 2 hours, 46 minutes. To attain a day only half as long again as this is considered to be tempting fate seriously. But the actual days of the planets as now observed are in no case shorter than two and a half times the calculated limits, so none of the solar family is expected to split a gut in our time — not even dizzy Saturn, which now comes the closest.

When you get to know Jupiter better, you discover that this bully boy's spinning is not uniform: his day is twisted, averaging some five minutes shorter at his equator than at his poles because his temperate and polar zones lag behind his tropics in their rate of turning. This is possible only because his visible surface is completely volatile, being just the upper deck of an atmosphere so huge the earth would be lost in it like a pea in a dish of whipped cream. And some of his latitudinal bands turn out to be super jet streams (many times swifter than those on Earth) outlined by the disparate westerly gales and cyclonic hurricanes perpetually fluting new channels all around his mighty girth.

Until this century, many astronomers thought Jupiter must be red hot from the pressure of his great mass and that his bands and rolling spots literally glowed from within. But as shadows cannot show on a red-hot poker, the photographed shadows of Jovian moons etched so sharply upon his clouds definitely proved him to be at least a good deal cooler than that. Then the difficult modern techniques of taking celestial temperatures were perfected enough to establish Jupiter's visible surface as ranging between 200° F. and 300° F. below zero.

The revelation of this bitter cold also threw new light on the mysterious pattern of absorption lines in Jupiter's spectral signature, the like of which had never been seen in any earthly analysis of chemical compounds. Careful work at length disclosed that "exactly the same absorption spectrum appeared when light passed through ammonia (NH_3) and methane (CH_4) gas for a considerable distance," identifying these two gases as the main components of the outer Jovian atmosphere. Then it was discovered that free radicals (elusive molecular fragments that normally exist for only a few thousandths of a second during chemical reactions) could be preserved by deep freezing and that the imine radical (NH), for example, congeals into a beautiful blue solid at − 193° F. while decomposed hydrazine (N_2H_4) freezes yellow at − 288° F., both colors perfectly matching blue and yellow bands on Jupiter.

As a result, according to Professor Francis Owen Rice, head of the Chemistry Department of Catholic University of America:

It seems almost certain that sunlight shining on Jupiter continuously generates free radicals in its outer atmosphere. On the basis of laboratory experience we can say that absorption of sunlight by the planet's methane and ammonia should liberate radicals such as CH_3, CH_2, NH_2, NH, NH_2NH and so on. Swept down rapidly to the colder depths of the planet's atmosphere by its great winds, the free radicals would be preserved there for, as we have seen, some of them at least are stable at low temperatures. This storing of sunlight in the form of high energy radicals deep in Jupiter's atmosphere would be analogous to the storage of sunlight in the form of coal in the earth (through the photosynthesis of ancient plants).

Not only might such a hoard provide a space ship visiting Jupiter with "an abundant supply of rocket fuel *par excellence* to refuel for the return journey to earth" but it introduces a whole new realm of chemistry which, although built of the same elements found on Earth, is full of more-or-less unearthly substances and potentialities, some of which may contain the keys to kinds of energy and life as yet undreamed by man.

♈   ♉   ♊   ♋   ♌   ♍

So far, only small beginnings have been made toward constructing a general theory of Jupiter's evolution, mostly on the basis of the known and deduced abundances of elements like hydrogen there. The fact that Jupiter is sufficiently far from the sun to be cold enough to condense the plentiful primordial hydrogen in immense quantities — particularly in the relatively sticky compounds of water (H_2O) and ammonia (NH_3) and the liquid methane (CH_4) — seems to be what gave him such capacity for growth. And once he had grown, his gravity must have enabled him to grab and hold still other gases like helium that would have escaped a smaller planet. In this way Jupiter's bulk must have waxed rapidly bigger and bigger, attaining majority in about a hundred million years, leaving only the decreasing quantities of gases beyond his reach for the remoter giants of Saturn, Uranus and Neptune.

The fact that Jupiter has an average density about the same as cheese, only a third heavier than water, strongly supports this concept of his preponderantly hydrogenic composition — especially since the pressure at his center (thirty million times that of earthly air) must give him a heavy core. A recent consensus among chemical-minded astronomers, in fact, has postulated a small Jovian core of highly compressed and hot metallic rock surrounded by successive layers of warm superdense H_2O "ice," possibly tepid solid helium, solid ammonia and a sea of liquid methane, the mountainous waves of which are driven by the perpetual storms of his raging atmosphere, which may consist of earthlike watery clouds at the lower levels surmounted by soaring cirrus crests of ice crystals that melt into downdrafts of torrential rain and, many miles higher, dense ammonia clouds floating on clear methane and composed of liquid droplets that congeal to wisps of ammonia crystals at the very top. As if such a cosmic ferment of uric-flavored marsh gas were not enough, Jupiter must also include many minor compounds such as cuprene (created by ultra-violet light striking methane) which, whirling about in his ammonic clouds, could account for some of the reddish streaks we see. Or sodium blended with ammonia that might well tint his great bands of grayish blue.

The turbulent interactions continuously embroiling the Jovian atmosphere must, of course, generate superthunderstorms and catastrophic typhoon-blizzards of a violence scarcely conceivable to Earthians, with inevitable magnetic storms reaching for hundreds of thousands of miles into his outer radiation belts. Radio telescopes indeed have furnished strong evidence of these disturbances by reacting more loudly to Jupiter's voice than to anything else in all the heavens. In the words of Harvard radio-astronomer Gerald Hawkins, "Jupiter is the performer that really dominates the air. When heard over a high-fidelity system, his roars and rumbles almost convince one that the Romans were right in their ideas about the gods." The force of Jupiter's radio source, whatever it is, has recently been estimated to reach 10,000 megawatts during its most violent bursts, but so far the radio astronomers can do little more than guess at what originates the complex, sporadic waves (mostly between 10 and 1000 megacycles) that arrive on Earth often circularly polarized as well as twinkling (like starlight) from the ionospheric wrinkles that refract them on the way.

There is of course plenty of leeway for the imagination in speculating as to what it would be like to be caught in a storm on Jupiter amid his sticky greenish snowflakes of crystallized ammonia which, as they whirl downward for hundreds of miles, steadily grow bigger by collisions until they may resemble mattresses or perhaps eventually giant bombers swooping wantonly through the black depths only to splash at last into the nightmarish methane ocean. But we scarcely need imagination to visualize the moiling, effervescent upper surfaces where we can, by Jove, actually see the tracks of his rampaging hurricanes through modern telescopes and pick out his trade winds with their frenzied hourly shiftings of form and color as the bloated giant whirls dizzily on his way, the snakelike polar fronts, even the jovial horse latitudes and, significantly, one or two mysterious spots or tropical whorls that linger in view with a curious persistence over long periods of time.

There is the Great Red Spot, for instance, first described in 1664 by Robert Hooke and still plain to see — a brick-red oval 30,000 miles long near Jupiter's equator, which sometimes fades to orange, then to brown, now moves north a little, now south, occasionally lurches almost 90° east or west of its mean abode yet somehow always remembers in the end to return to its original stamping ground. A lesser spot, known as the South Tropical Disturbance, has behaved with even greater license, circling wantonly around the entire 270,000 miles of equator about every two years since the turn of the century. But sometimes these two spots have seemed to chase each other, dodging and jockeying along side by side, dancing a little, then reluctantly separating so the South Tropical Disturbance could complete another biennial tour. In 1949, however, after fifty romping years, the latter faded from view altogether, perhaps submerged or dispersed by some invisible influence and, to my knowledge, has not been seen since.

It has been postulated that these tremendous spots (each bigger than Earth) might really be clouds of volcanic dust belching upward from Jupiter's core or perhaps the manifestation of some unearthly type of storm. But why should a "volcanic" cloud circumnavigate Jupiter biennially? Or a storm last three centuries?

A California meteorologist, Dr. Yale Mintz, who noticed that every time the sun lets loose a large flare of ultra-violet light Jupiter breaks out in new spots, compares them to tropical high-altitude storms on Earth which are also triggered by sun flares and appear as spots to passing astronauts. One astronomer thinks the Great Red Spot could be a floating island of solid helium while a growing consensus prefers the theory that it is more likely a great wave of gas, either convex or concave, riding above some corresponding plateau or depression on Jupiter's hidden solid surface.

There has been less discussion about life on the boisterous planet, but surely life must be counted at least a possibility in a world with as much liquid water as Jupiter is credited with, even though most of it may be swirling about his atmosphere. And at some level in his lower clouds his temperature, increasing with the pressure of depth, is almost certainly moderate enough (perhaps also, for all we know, stable enough) to permit the evolution of complex organisms — conceivably swimming creatures which, if proportionable to their environment, might make the great blue whale look like a haddock.

The sixth planet from the sun is Saturn, almost as big as Jupiter but even more giddy and perhaps twice as gaseous. Weighing only seven tenths as much as water, she is literally more buoyant than a wooden croquet ball and would float high on any watery ocean large enough to support her.

To the ancient Greeks Saturn, oddly enough, personified Cronos or Father Time, lord of a golden age of innocence and plenty. But, from our modern telescopic perspective, the planet seems definitely feminine, like Saturnia (an ancient name for Italy), her main distinction being the broad-brimmed hoop of skirt engirdling her buxom waist.

I will never forget my first glimpse of Saturn through a large observatory telescope — an experience emotionally comparable to one's first solo flight — when she made me think of a fat Carmelite nun in white habit and wide-winged coif, her halo of spectral purity enclosing that magic round form that just floated serenely upon "nothing" — so delicate and so potent in her unassailable authority as a world far bigger than our own.

What is dynamically and chemically true of Jupiter should be generally true of Saturn also, her main distinctions being her unique ring system, her mass less than a third of his, and her temperature about 40° F. colder. Certainly her creamy vesture of methane and ammonic clouds in churning latitudinal bands is a near duplication of his tawny stripes, even to occasional bright spots beside her equator — though her frigid saturnalia appears both paler and more stable than his, probably because more of her whirling gases (particularly ammonia) have condensed into clouds and more of her fuming mists have frozen into snow.

One of the great mysteries connected with Saturn is the still unanswered question of how the ancient Maoris of New Zealand knew about her rings — for there is evidence that they did have a Saturn ring legend long before the days of Galileo. Could they have had concave parabolic mirrors in some long-forgotten civilization? Is it conceivable that they descended from a great "lost continent of Mu" in the Pacific Ocean that had advanced to the discovery of optical lenses before vanishing practically without a trace?

Far from reducing the number of Saturine mysteries, the large modern telescopes are raising new controversies as fast as they reveal new data. At first it was taken for granted that Saturn's rings must be made of the same stuff as their tumid mother, but gradually the realization came with better magnification that there was something very ethereal about them. Not only can one look clean through the rings in places but certain of their edges just dissolve gradually into the sky. The inmost ring is as of translucent crepe, very hard to see except by its faint shadow upon the planet, the colors of which show through it as pale yellow at the equator, turning more orange and reddish at higher latitudes and finally slightly green at the poles.

The rings are geometrically so perfect as to seem unnatural. They are absolutely smooth, continuous, and untarnished, and they lie in the exact plane of Saturn's equator. When tilted to their maximum of 28° in relation to the earth, they reflect nearly twice as much sunlight as does the planet proper, but virtually disappear for a day or two when edge on. It is believed that they must be less than ten miles thick and, some astronomers think, only a few inches. In any case little doubt remains that they are the flattest-known phenomenon in nature in relation to their thinness, which proportionately far exceeds the paper of this page.

You might think that the thin ice covering a great lake would be flatter and thinner than Saturn's rings. But no: such ice, however thin, must bulge convexly upwards like all the earth's liquid surface. The rings of Saturn, on the other hand, are absolutely flat for 500,000 miles around with a thickness at most only 1/17,000 of their outside diameter.

The material of the rings puzzled astronomers of the seventeenth and eighteenth centuries, but since then overwhelming evidence has demonstrated that they must be made of coarse dust, including a certain amount of ice in the form of crystals, perhaps formed around the dust. Obviously if they were single solid pieces like wheels, their outside edges would have to move faster than their inner edges as they turn about Saturn. But the spectroscope proves that their inside parts move faster, and exactly at the speeds required by Newton's law of gravitation and Kepler's laws of motion for numerous separate bodies in circular orbits. The spectroscope can readily measure the approach or recession of any light's source by separating the light into colors according to wave frequency or pitch, then measuring this frequency. In the same way, the changing pitch of a loco-

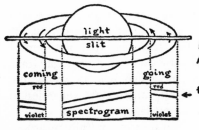

MOTIONS OF SATURN AND RINGS
AS ANALYZED BY SPECTROSCOPE

tilt of frequency lines reveals
that the inner rings move
faster than the outer ones

motive whistle (measured by your sense of hearing) tells you whether the train is coming or going. This is the well-known doppler principle mentioned earlier as a coming tool in space navigation.

The granular nature of Saturn's rings is revealed also by their great reflective power, powder reflecting more light than the same material in larger pieces, and from their average density, which has been calculated at less than $\frac{1}{800}$ of the very low density of Saturn proper. There may be occasional rocks in the outer ring, but it is believed that few of the particles are larger than small gravel or hail or sand, grading down to frosty dust at the inside edge. On the other hand, the rings could not very well be made of anything as tenuous as smoke, nor contain particles even as fine as white flour, else molecular motion or the pressure of sun ions would long since have dispersed or pushed them off into space.

In view of the modern theories of moon evolution, it is not hard to understand that Saturn's rings may well be the remains of a satellite that drew too close and cracked apart, to be slowly ground up in the Saturnine mills. The rings themselves, as seen from the planet, would now appear like cosmic grist wheels filling most of the sky and actually turning in both directions at once: the inner parts eastward (faster than the planet), the slower outer ones westward. And this curious performance is a clue to the differences in the rings, accounting for the fact that there are not just one or two rings but at least three, the divisions coming at the nodes of resonance.

To grasp the entire mechanism you need to visualize a modern superhighway, several lanes wide, running around the shores of a small circular island with thousands of cars driving along all the lanes in the same direction — the ones on the inside of the curve going the fastest. The laws of this speedway, of course, are Kepler's Laws of Planetary Motion, requiring that the inmost lane overcome its strongest gravity by greatest centrifugal force (produced by speed) while each successive lane outward goes more slowly, the whole flow of traffic tapering its velocities in progressive stages to the gentle outermost lane.

Each ring of Saturn, indeed, has been spectroscopically measured to have definite speed limits: a minimum speed as well as a maximum. If any particle in any ring could fail to respect either of these limits, it would automatically and literally be expelled from the ring, pressed either outwards or inwards according to whether centrifugal force or gravity had the greater influence. And as if it were not remarkable enough for each revolving ring thus to have its separate range of speeds, there are the gap speeds which are arbitrarily forbidden to any of them by resonance, these taboo velocities being interspersed in the gaps between the graduated speed zones much as if cars were prevented from crossing from the 20–30 m.p.h. lane of the highway to the 40–50 m.p.h. lane by invisible, infallible cops who pounced on anyone traveling at a speed between 30 and 40 m.p.h. and eliminated him.

The separations between the rings thus created by traffic-speed enforcement are called Kirkwood's gaps, after Daniel Kirkwood, who in the 1860's defined the principle of orbital resonance, one of the major influences in the music of the spheres. In this application of Kirkwood's principle, it soon became clear that particles probably once occupied the ring gaps and would still be there if it were not for the almost invisible police action of the inner Saturnian moons, which, from scores of thousands of miles away, wield their magical influence — not with threats like traditional cops but with subtle gravity exerted in compound waves of vibration that are just as impossible to resist as the melodies of the Pied Piper.

The key to these potent harmonies of Saturn, then, is the node, which astronomically is a line of conjunction between force fields as musically it is a zone of rest in a vibrating body. It is also the very same influence, described in Chapter 3, that plucked the umbilical chord of our own moon when she first swung free of her mother earth, and that imposes the strict equation $(I + 2G = 3E)$ among Jupiter's Galilean moons (page 87). It is a syzygy of rhythms among the worlds, a sympathy of vibration like that familiar push used to help a friend swinging in a swing. If the moving swing has a natural period of two seconds and you give a push regularly every two seconds, your friend will swing farther and go higher. Most other push intervals would not help the swinging because they would form discords unsympathetic to the swing's slow "vibration" rate, but simple multiples of two seconds would help, such as 4, 6 or 8 seconds. And a few fractions too, like 1, ½, or maybe even ⅔, ⅚ second, and so on, to a slight extent.

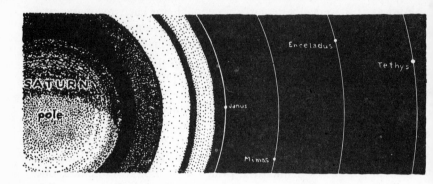

In the same manner, Kirkwood's gaps were pushed out largely by Saturn's four inmost moons, Janus, Mimas, Enceladus and Tethys, a quartet of cosmopolitan troubadours who tuned in on all ring particles to which they were harmonically related. Their main chorus was directed upon what is now the largest gap, called Cassini's division, which separates the two bright rings by some 2,500 miles. This is where the ring particles once moved in a circuit period (month) of slightly more than eleven hours — which happens to be about two thirds of Janus' period, one half of Mimas' period, one third that of Enceladus, and one fourth that of Tethys. As Janus and Enceladus thus combined their pull every third time that the eleven-hour particles revolved around Saturn, Mimas and Tethys every fourth time, Mimas and Enceladus every sixth time, and at least three moons in unison every twelfth time, gradually the gap was cleared to its present dimensions and, by more modest harmonies in the lesser gaps, the rings were made plural and musically molded to exactly what we see there today.

The farther out we go from the sun the weaker must be the patriarchal leash of gravity. And in the case of the seventh planet the solar lassitude may have contributed to the curious fact that Uranus rotates on his axis almost at right angles to all the other planets, giving him extreme seasons of continuous light and darkness lasting up to forty years. This phenomenon may be a relic also of a close shave with some large passing body in the remote past, for it includes all five of the Uranian moons, which circle like choir boys right over his equator.

Uranus (named after Urania, the muse of astronomy) is actually visible to the naked eye but, being of the sixth magnitude, is so faint he was not "discovered" until 1781 when William Herschel, appropriately a professional musician as well as an amateur astronomer of Bath, England, noticed a "comet" among the stars of Gemini. A check of the Royal Observatory records, however, quickly revealed that the same object had been seen and recorded more than twenty times in the preceding century, each time as a star, and its slow plodding pace across the heavens, now proved through its successive positions, soon established it as a planet circling twice as far from the sun as the remotest previously known planet, Saturn.

When astronomers later tried to calculate Uranus' exact orbit, making precise allowance for the disturbing effects of Saturn and Jupiter, they found that the observed positions of Uranus never came out quite as Newton's equation of gravity said they should, the accumulative error by 1843 amounting to an intolerable two minutes of arc.

What could be the matter? Was there still another planet up there somewhere pulling Uranus off course? A student of astronomy at Cambridge University named John Couch Adams believed this so strongly that he actually computed the position of the hypothetical world in 1845 by "inverse perturbations" deduced from the facts then known about Uranus. Somehow this unprecedented intellectual accomplishment failed to stir the British Astronomer Royal to look for a new planet, and the following year Urbain Leverrier of the Paris Observatory, who knew nothing of Adams' work, virtually duplicated it, with the

successful result that the eighth planet, Neptune, was actually
spotted by telescope in Berlin on the night of September 23, 1846.

This classic episode in astronomical history was a doubly tri-
umphant demonstration of the cosmic validity of the law of
gravitation. And it was repeated again in the present century
when small residue perturbations in the orbits of both Uranus
and Neptune required the presence of a ninth planet, Pluto,
which was finally revealed to Clyde Tombaugh on March 13, 1930,
after a quarter-century's search inaugurated by Percival Lowell,
whose initials are immortalized in the first two letters of its
name, as is Tombaugh's name in the last two.

THE THREE OUTER PLANETS

Both Uranus and Neptune are naturally in the class of giant
planets, having diameters about four times Earth's. Their chem-
istries and densities closely resemble those of Jupiter except that,
being colder, their ammonia is more condensed, leaving them
the residue of gaseous methane and free radicals that gives Neptune his appropriate sea-green pallor.

Pluto, on the other hand, being probably smaller than
Mars and an ignominious speck even through the 200-inch telescope, shows no sign of having received any appreciable portion of the primordial hydrogen spilling from the sun, and some
astronomers suspect he may be not a born planet at all but a
moon that "got away" from Neptune, just as Mercury in like
manner could have once served as a moon for Venus. Not only
is Pluto's orbit an ellipse more elongated than any other planet's
but it passes inside (and almost intersects) the nearly circular pathway of Neptune. Gerard Kuiper thinks Pluto probably won his
promotion from an orbit around Neptune as a result of the giant
planet's loss of gravitational mass through evaporation during his

early stages of solidifying. This is suggested further by Pluto's lazy rotational period of six days: suspiciously long for a planet but just about right for a moon of Neptune that (as moons are wont to do) revolved as fast as it rotated by keeping the same face always turned toward its primary.

Whether the solar system harbors any planets beyond Pluto is an open question, but it seems unlikely that there are any major ones that far out in view of the trend toward smallness among the known hub and rim planets.

Beyond the sun's influence altogether, there seem likely to be countless myriads of planets in all directions, although their presence at such a range can only be deduced (not seen) by known methods of science. The most definite nonsolar planet so far generally accepted is revolving around Barnard's runner, a dim star only six light-years away and famous for having the fastest apparent motion across the sky of any star. This "dark companion," about half again as big as Jupiter, is without question a planet. But others known to be circling around 61 Cygni, Lalande 21185 and other stars are several times bigger, with the result that some astronomers consider them really baby stars. The smaller and darker they are, of course, the more likely they are to remain undiscovered, yet they must exist in some percentage of stars, and even if in only one star out of a thousand, the Milky Way alone would contain better than a hundred million planetary systems. That should provide possibilities enough to satisfy the most pessimistic that there is virtually certain to be life comparable to ours in many parts of the sky — and, according to the statistical law of probability, a fair percentage of the life will turn out to be more advanced than anything yet developed on Earth. Indeed, it was for the very purpose of getting in touch with this outside intelligence that the new National Radio Astronomy Observatory at Green Bank, West Virginia, began in 1960 its Project Ozma to listen seriously and methodically for artificial radio signals, for some sort of improbable sequence of impulses — in short, for a significantly patternful message from the spheres.

5. Gadflies of the void

IF YOU, DOWN THERE, should suppose that the only solid bodies that pass between the earth and the sun are Venus, Mercury and our moon, you would not be entirely correct. For there are lots of minor worlds, not massive enough to be called planets yet not moons either, that swing inside the earth's orbit, also inside Venus' ethereal bower and sometimes even inside the cramped precincts of Mercury.

The heaviest of these bodies are the asteroids or, more logically, planetoids (minor planets), varying in size from a medium moon to a soaring Rock of Gibraltar. Smaller ones are meteorites. And bigger, lighter ones, made of practically nothing but a frozen nucleus that evaporates into glowing gas when near the sun, are comets.

Although Kepler and many other astronomers had hunted during the seventeenth and eighteenth centuries for the "missing planet" between Mars and Jupiter in their efforts to tie together the disjointed music of the spheres, it was not until the first night of the nineteenth century (January 1, 1801) that Giuseppe

Piazzi of Palermo stumbled upon a seventh-magnitude "star" that had changed its position westward since the night before. After watching it for several months, during which time it stopped moving west and turned east, he wrote Bode that he had discovered a new "planet" — perhaps the missing one that would make Bode's Law complete. Before the letter was delivered, however, and before he had determined the planet's orbit, Piazzi fell sick and his discovery escaped behind the sun.

It was only the work of a brilliant young German mathematician named Karl Friedrich Gauss (of whom we will hear more) that enabled Piazzi to find the "planet" again when it re-entered the night sky at the end of the year. And its orbit was thus revealed to occupy just the region between Mars and Jupiter that Kepler had predicted must contain a planet — and Bode was overjoyed at the apparent fulfillment of his law.

When the new "planet" turned out to be only 480 miles in diameter, however, Piazzi, naturally disappointed, named it after a female deity: Ceres of the harvest. Then when another little body was discovered a year later and two more in the next five years, all were named in similar vein: Pallas, Juno and Vesta. Although no more turned up for a generation, there was a burst of discoveries in 1847, and the rate has been increasing ever since. Following the first three hundred asteroids, all named after mythological characters (mostly female), each one has been given at least a number, and the total now known is approaching 30,000 at the rate of several new ones every night, the undiscovered ones still outnumbering the discovered by an estimated ten to one. Without modern photography it obviously would not be possible to keep track of such a swarm. And, even so, much of the work is done by the Recheninstitut in Berlin, which has been operating for more than sixty years as a special clearinghouse for asteroids.

The weirdness of these elfish orbs can be suggested by the fact that little Ceres is by far the biggest one known. Her nearest rival, Pallas, is a mere 300 miles thick. Then comes Vesta, who, although the only asteroid bright enough to be seen with the naked eye (if you know exactly when and where to look), is but 240 miles in diameter, and Juno half that. Almost all the others are less than 50 miles thick, the estimates having to be based on the amount of light reflected. And the density of asteroids must be correspondingly small to avoid observable perturbations in the orbit of Mars, the total weight of all their thousands (known and unknown) being estimated at only one percent of the earth's.

Of course, one must not visualize these demiworlds as being little round replicas of Earth or Venus or Jupiter, for they are much too small to be able to hold on to an atmosphere, and almost all are very irregular in shape. This is surmised from the even rhythm of their variations in brightness as they rotate and has been generally accepted as evidence that they are not aggregations of tiny particles or condensed droplets, which would almost certainly have gradually built up smooth spheres, but rather are jagged chunks of a once-large planet that somehow broke into many pieces, perhaps because of the tidal forces of Jupiter.

This hypothesis is supported also by the asteroids' orbits, which, with a few exceptions, converge closely enough to suggest a common point of origin between Mars and Jupiter. And it is hardly contradicted by the fact that a few out of so many susceptible busybodies should show signs of having at some time fallen under the gravitational influence either of neighboring Mars or potent Jupiter, both of whom, it seems more than likely, have thus actually tamed wild asteroids into docile moons.

Certainly the bias of Jove is evidenced by the strong tendency of these nomads to let their nearest and farthest points from the sun come at similar locations. And they show definite Kirkwood gaps on a much larger scale than the rings of Saturn, their teeming orbits conspicuously avoiding those solar distances at which their periods of revolution would be a half, a third, two fifths, etc., of Jupiter's own year — converts from such fractions presumably being the source of at least a few of the smaller Jovian satellites.

But the music of these great and tenuous asteroidal rings, which reach invisibly all the way around the sun and the four inner planets, is revealed not only negatively through nodal gaps but also positively in definite concentration points where the celestial gnomes are most numerous. Two of these places were predicted by the mathematician Joseph-Louis Lagrange, even before the discovery of asteroids, in his famous conclusion regarding the difficult "three-body problem" that "the vertices of an equilateral triangle form a stable configuration." Indeed, he implemented this theoretical solution, for which no celestial example was then known, by imaginatively postulating "a small body moving around the sun in such a way that its distances from Jupiter and the sun would remain equal to the radius of Jupiter's orbit." And of this intellectual figment at the third corner of the equilateral Jovian triangle, he explained that, even if it be disturbed, it would just oscillate around the vertex which is its harmonic home.

How thrilled would Lagrange have been if he could have witnessed the discovery of Achilles in 1904 and the proof of his beautiful concept in the dozen other asteroids now known to occupy just the nodes he specified, literally forming vertices at the required radial distances, seven of them before and five of them behind Jupiter — acting in this case not as moons but as little brothers of the planetary king. With each of their members bearing the name of a Homeric hero, these two delegations are appropriately known as the Trojans. And they revolve grandiosely around the great sun every twelve years while respectfully circulating at the same time about those mystic nodes just 484 million miles before and after Jupiter where their deputized authority can hardly be disputed even by the gravitational blandishments of Saturn, who passes slightly closer to them than Jupiter once each twenty years.

It is considered likely that in the early days of the solar system there were hundreds of times more asteroids than now remain and that, as they wheeled about the vast interplanetary skies like migrating birds, their numbers were steadily diminished by the slow grinding action of tides and collisions and near collisions over billions of years, the resulting randomized orbits bringing a certain percentage of them each millennium into the atmospheres of planets and the sun to be bogged by friction and eventually merged into the bulk of the major worlds.

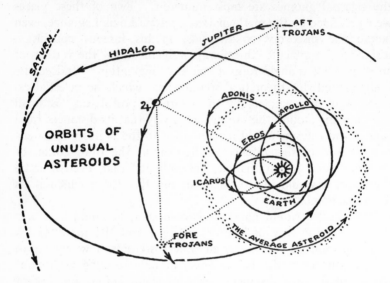

Most of the relatively few survivors of this relentless process are naturally those with the most strait-laced and conservative orbits, leaving only the handful of erratic ones currently champing at their aphelions just beyond Jupiter's gravitational lasso (like wild Hidalgo) or pushing their perihelions within Mercury's scanty beat (like swooping Icarus) or perhaps tempting fate in wanton swipes at Earth (like tiny Hermes, who brushed by us at 300,000 miles in 1937, almost as close as the moon). Of all the asteroids, however, Eros is probably the most interesting and useful. He is roughly shaped like a brick some 21 miles long, 10 wide and 5 thick, which rotates about its shortest axis. Astronomers particularly appreciate him as a sort of celestial benchmark because he regularly swings close enough to Earth

to provide the largest usable parallax for accurately measuring the sun's distance. And being bigger than either of Mars' moons yet practically free of gravity, Eros is an obvious candidate for an early, easy destination for the pioneering space ships. In fact he could well become the first outside world actually to feel the strange tread of man, perhaps as soon as 1975, when he is due for his next rendezvous with the earth!

If you wonder what it would be like literally to touch an asteroid, you might consider a not-unrelated phenomenon that happened right on the earth on February 2, 1922, when a Negro sharecropper named Ed Bush, near Baldwyn, Mississippi, heard a strange humming in the sky which he thought must be an airplane. Looking up, he was surprised to see only blue emptiness. But the humming rapidly increased into a rush of air that ended suddenly when a dark stone thudded upon the ground about ten feet away, burying itself three or four inches into soft clay.

Running to tell the plantation owner, Judge Allen Cox, Ed brought him back in a few minutes to see his "stone from the sky." The judge picked it up. It weighed about a pound and, as the judge reported it afterwards, "was still hot. Not hot enough to burn, but very decidedly warm, and it gave off a smell like brimstone or a flint when it has been struck with steel."

Such are the rare cases of meteorites seen to land on earth. Meteorites, so far as is known, are just small editions of the asteroids and the only definitely unearthly things that humans can pick up and handle and analyze in a laboratory. Being billions of times more numerous than asteroids and, to a much greater extent, at the mercy of any atmospheres they happen to enter, they naturally are a good deal more apt to be captured by Earth. But since meteorites naturally increase in numbers as they scale down in size, the great majority of them are mere pebbles rather than stones or boulders. And of course as the

scale continues farther downward they soon become grains so
tiny that the friction of striking the atmosphere burns them
up completely. These brief apparitions are traditionally called
meteors and are the common "shooting stars" familiar to anyone who goes outdoors at night. They evidently got their name
from the Greek *meteoros*, "above the air," probably without
serious thought that such "golden apples" dropping from the
tree of heaven in Atlas' garden of the Hesperides might sometime come all the way down to Earth and be touched by mortal
men.

The modern word meteorite, as now used in science, applies
to the material body as distinct from the luminous appearance
of these objects, that is, to any celestial unit smaller than an
asteroid, which would mean, roughly, less than a few hundred
feet in diameter. But there seems to be no defined line between
asteroids and meteorites for the understandable reason that bodies
of such bordering magnitudes are historically so rare the question
has never come up.

The earliest meteorite in history was recorded in China in
644 B.C., and probably the earliest in the West was the famous
"stony star" that fell in Aegospotami, Thrace, in 466 B.C. Such
objects were located so rarely that they were naturally considered
divine — the apports of gods — even up to the nineteenth century. Indeed, the Ephesians are described in the Bible as worship-
ping their great goddess Diana in the person of her "image which
fell down from Jupiter" (Acts xix.35). The famous black stone
in the Kaaba at Mecca, venerated by the Moslems, is almost
certainly a meteorite. And in Chihuahua, Mexico, a meteoric
iron weighing nearly two tons was found, wrapped in mummy
cloth, in a Montezuma grave.

By the nineteenth century, however, science had come to dis-
trust miracles on principle, and when "a shower of stones fell
out of a clear sky onto a quiet village in Gascony," the French
Academy replied to the detailed report signed by three hundred
witnesses with "regret that in our enlightened age there can still
be people so superstitious as to believe stones fall from the sky."
Even President Thomas Jefferson, a broad-minded naturalist, on

receiving a request in 1807 from two professors in Connecticut for permission to excavate a freshly fallen stone, declined with the comment, "It is more likely that two Yankee professors are lying than that a stone fell from the sky."

Yet now, a century and a half later, we have dozens of authenticated observations of meteorites landing on Earth and some 1,400 known meteorites in the world's museums and exhibits ranging from greenish-black pebbles called tektites to the 60-ton block of iron which still lies where it fell in Hoba West, Grootfontein, South Africa. New ones are being discovered at the rate of about twenty-five a year out of the few chunks that actually reach solid ground — most of which, of course, must be lost in forests, deserts, glaciers, lakes and oceans.

All of those smaller than very coarse sand when they hit the atmosphere are inevitably and invisibly roasted away in a fraction of a second by the sudden heat of impact. This includes probably more than 99.999 percent of the dozen-odd tons of space debris that daily are believed to collide with Earth — mainly in the form of an estimated 750 quadrillion microscopic and nearly microscopic particles of dust spread throughout the solar system to the unimaginable thinness of less than a hundred pounds in each volume of space the size of Earth. Even this tenuity, however, is some thousands of times denser than most interstellar dust beyond the solar system, and it is by no means evenly distributed.

Thus, although meteors coarse enough to flare into terrestrial visibility are traveling through space with an average separation of about 250 miles, this interval may pack down to 25 miles or less during "meteor showers." The normal bright meteor you see in the sky, according to Fred Whipple, the authority in this field, is actually the vaporization of an object smaller than a pea, and it hits the upper air at between 7 and 50 miles a second. It may start to glow as high as 100 miles from the ground and usually is at peak intensity when about 60 miles up, quickly oxidizing into fine ash and disappearing by the time it is within 30 or 40 miles of Earth — except in rare cases.

Of course, one could not see a light the size of a pea 100 miles away. The meteor is visible only because of its brilliant flare-up to an intense white blaze a foot or more in diameter, produced by the terrific friction, and the fact of its speed making that sudden dramatic streak scores of miles long, which may linger as a hollow luminous cylinder for several seconds before the ionization has dissipated.

The speed of entry into the atmosphere has to be at least 7 miles a second, which the earth's gravitation alone would impart. Unless the meteorite is overtaking us, some of the earth's orbital velocity of 18.5 miles a second must also be added — not to mention the earth's rotational speed. And then there is the speed of the meteorite in relation to the sun, which can be as high as 26 miles a second at our solar distance without forcing it out of the system altogether. Therefore, if the meteorite is moving around the sun counter-earthwise (which relatively few are) and everything adds up to the maximum, it could strike the terrestrial air at close to 50 miles a second.

Any higher speed would indicate the body had come from outside the solar system, but there is no accepted evidence that this has occurred, and the highest measured meteor velocity (by triangulation) so far is 46 miles a second, with the average coming to about 25 m.p.s. The redder, slower, more widely separated ones appear mostly before midnight and the faster, hotter, bluer ones arrive in the morning. The reason for this disparity, of course, is that during the P.M. hours you are riding the rear half of the earth where only the meteors that overtake it can appear, while in the A.M. hours you advance around the forward terrestrial face where the addition of head-on collisions approximately doubles the numbers and velocities.

Notwithstanding the fact that meteorites produce a white heat as they stab into the atmospheric wall, the heat is almost entirely swept off their sizzling surfaces by the ferocious impact of the air as it jerks them to a virtual halt. In consequence, stones large enough to reach the ground are apt to land at subsonic speeds, as Ed Bush noticed in Mississippi, when the coolth of their interiors will absorb so much of their residue surface heat that they can be handled immediately without discomfort. The bigger they are, in fact, the cooler they will be as soon as the heat has had time to equalize, for the large ones naturally retain much more of the interplanetary cold. Indeed, it is recorded that one of the biggest pieces of the great meteorite that fell in Dhurmsala, India, in 1860, was "found in moist earth half an hour after the fall, coated with ice." Another sky stone landed so gently one winter near Hassle in Sweden that it bounced off the ice of a lake without breaking it, then came to rest without appreciably melting it.

Considering that each square mile of earthly surface receives an estimated average of only one meteorite every thousand years, it is not surprising that people almost never get hit by them. Nor need one wonder that there is no record of anyone's having been killed by a meteorite in all history, although such a distinguished fate is steadily getting more and more likely and is bound to happen eventually, as we shall presently see. As a matter of fact, there have already been a number of significantly close shaves, mind you — like the time a large stone hit the earth between two carters on a road at Charsonville, France, the impact heaving the ground up six feet high beside them; a few cases of houses damaged; and an unverified report of a Japanese girl struck and wounded half a century ago.

The classic case of meteorite injury, however, and the first fully authenticated instance on record of any human being hit by something out of another world, is the recent episode of Mrs. Ann Elizabeth Hodges of Sylacauga, Alabama. A plump housewife of thirty-two, she was taking a noontide nap covered with two quilts on a sofa in her one-story frame house early in December 1954 when suddenly a "brilliant fireball" streaked downward from the western sky, making a trail of smoke that was seen by hundreds of people as far away as Mississippi and Georgia. Over Alabama it exploded (probably from the pressure and heat) and a boom "like thunder" drew heads out of windows for fifty miles around as the separate pieces and molten spherules fell over the wood-patched farmland.

Mrs. Hodges did not hear the burst in the sky but was awakened shortly afterward with an unaccountable shock. As she recalled it later, "Mama came running in" from the next room "and asked me if the house was falling down. I said I didn't know. I thought it was the chimney. I got up and started out of the house. Then my hip began hurting."

Just after that, the two women noticed the jagged hole in the ceiling and found a black, nine-pound stone on the floor. They were quite excited, but it was nothing to the reaction of the world outside. Within a couple of minutes "neighbors came flooding into the house, followed by cops and more neighbors." A doctor took Mrs. Hodges to his office to x-ray her space wounds but found only bruises on her hip and hand. Maxwell Air Base in Montgomery, fifty miles to the south, sent forty airplanes out looking for the wreckage of "a burning airliner." A couple of hours later, an Air Force helicopter landed in the Sylacauga schoolyard, and its crew took charge of the "angular rhombus" meteorite.

When Hulitt Hodges came home tired and hungry from his job as a tree surgeon, his wife greeted him as gently as she could. "We had a little excitement around here," she began. "A meteor fell through the roof." But Hulitt Hodges quickly reddened into a fury of frustration. Not only did he have a bruised wife, a hole in his roof and hundreds of people tramping open-mouthed through his living room, but the stone that caused it all, "his" meteorite, had been "stolen" without his even seeing it.

The ensuing fuss and commotion were not much eased by the mounting stream of telegrams, long-distance phone calls, photographers, reporters, buyer's agents and a lawyer who convinced Hodges that the elusive stone from space was worth "possibly five thousand dollars." As Mrs. Hodges retired late in the evening to a hospital with an attack of nerves, she had just enough strength to answer a reporter's final question: how does it feel to be the first person in the world hit by a shooting star?

Said Ann Hodges, "I feel bruised."

If the chances of some human somewhere getting hit in a hundred years are "only three out of ten," as figured by meteorite expert Lincoln La Paz of the University of New Mexico, obviously such a score could apply only to people below the meteoric rampart of the ionosphere. Out where I am in airless space, on the other hand, it is strikingly different. Here we must face all the sub-pea-size pebbles and grains and grit that would burn up before reaching Earth. Even though they are much smaller than some of the big ones that last all the way to the ground, these little space nuts are a billion times more numerous and moving a hundred times faster than any earthly bullets. Certainly they are a ponderable hazard that must be reckoned in the price of interplanetary freedom.

So we are grateful to Dr. Whipple for inventing the "meteor bumper," already standard equipment on nearly all manned space ships projected or under construction. It is a guard made of thin metal sheeting placed an inch or so outside the ship's hull to shatter "99 out of 100 small meteors."

At first thought, one would not suppose any object moving dozens of miles per second could be stopped in an inch. But Whipple explains that all but the biggest of these kernels will explode so completely and instantaneously in the intense heat of impact that no molecular structure describable as solid will survive the bumper, only a harmless powdery splash reaching the ship itself in the borderline cases. It is simple enough, of course, for a physicist to calculate how much kinetic heat each size and speed of meteorite will produce and therefore to what depth it can volatilize the metal of bumper or hull.

Even the exceptional bodies that are massive enough to penetrate the main skin of the space ship need not necessarily do serious damage if they don't happen to strike a transistor or a human head, for self-sealing devices will automatically plug a leak and pressure-sensitive alarms can warn of emergencies. A case in point is the report from space rocket Pioneer V that in its first 1,040,000 miles of travel around the sun it had "87 slight impacts from micrometeorites and 5 heavier ones . . . but nothing really damaging." However, if Whipple is anywhere near right in his prognosis that even a bumper-equipped space station 250 feet in diameter will actually be punctured by meteorites about twice a month, the long-range hazard of those gadflies must be taken very seriously. The white heat produced by their velocity can be so explosive, despite their small caliber, that to be hit by one may feel more like a thunderbolt than a bullet. And there is no doubt, at least, that the problem must be lived with and settled in its fashion just as men have had to go on living for months in a leaky submarine or under fire on a military front.

Of course this problem may never be completely "solved" in the sense that the problem of a cold room is solved by a stove. For it brings into play a larger realm of nature and a megaworld of speeds and relationships to which no known form of life (with the possible exception of dry spores) has so far adapted itself or perhaps ever seriously tried. An inkling of what is involved can be had by considering the recent frightening case of the squadron of jet fighters that flew almost head on through the middle of another formation of jets without any of the pilots noticing it! Yet a speed differential of mach 2 (twice the speed of sound) is almost like standing still compared to the differences inherent in a meeting of space vehicles. Here the permissible margin of navigational error shrinks almost to zero. To be as much as one second late in a rendezvous with a space station, unless you have closely matched its speed beforehand, almost inevitably puts the station out of sight, a situation not solved by its continued recession at whatever disparity in miles per second still separates your speeds.

Even when improved radio devices for "homing in" and automatic speed-blenders designed to avoid such errors have become standard space equipment, the increase in speed differentials as astronautical evolution unfolds is bound to cause serious meeting mishaps, including collisions. And a space collision obviously will seldom be the gentle sideswipe of the earthly highway which you can "see coming" but will more likely strike completely without warning — producing a lightninglike disintegration from explosive friction and heat, with death mercifully instantaneous to all. Each succeeding crash, of course, must compound the overall danger by adding new derelicts to the entropy of the universe.

The basic problem of developing safeguards against any kinds of collision in space turns out to be a surprisingly profound one — as if so by divine intent — for thus far none of the experts has been able to get around what is called the "paradox of proximity," a strange and immutable mathematical law which evidently makes the unavoidability of collision increase directly in proportion to the combined speed of approach of any two objects. Although slow-moving ships at sea can normally recognize a collision situation in time to avoid it, even they sometimes misjudge and hit head on. Cars and airplanes have more trouble, despite better-defined traffic lanes and stricter "rules of the road." But high-speed rockets and space ships that do not keep exactly to the lanes and speed bands assigned them will be definitely at God's mercy so far as collisions are concerned, neither telescopes nor radar being able to warn them in time. Dodging a meteorite intentionally (unless you are lucky enough to be within much less than a mile a second of matching it in velocity) is considered absolutely impossible by known means.

The reason is that the bearing between any two "straight-moving" collision-bound bodies or vehicles remains constant, while the bearing between two vehicles that will pass each other closely remains so nearly constant until so late that by the time any bearing change is definitely recognizable it is too late to act unless the approach speed is slow, the degree of required slowness depending on your perceptiveness of bearing change, rapidity of decision and maneuverability of your own vehicle. To sidestep danger by "evasive action" ahead of time "just to be on the safe side" is clearly out of the question, because any such random maneuver is as likely to bring you toward a collsion as away from one, especially with the intentions (if any) of the other vehicle unknown.

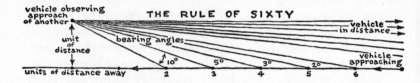

For example, the bearing of an approaching object headed to miss you by a full mile will change only one degree in closing from 12 to 10 miles' range, which (with current flight instruments) is hardly enough of a change on which to base reliable judgment. Accelerating relatively slowly, the bearing will change but 2° in closing from 6 to 5 miles, 3° from 5 to 4, 5° from 4 to 3, and 10° from 3 to 2. As the product of the three figures in each of these last four cases equals 60, the strange mathematical law has been called the "Rule of Sixty in Motion." This holds true down to two miles or twice the passing distance in whatever units it is measured. But it is obvious that as the time available for perception, decision and evasion diminishes while the rate of bearing change increases, the surer you are of which way to dodge, the less time you have for dodging. And if there is no telling whether an object is going to hit you or miss you by a mile until it is only a few seconds away, even an atheist would have to admit that prayer is at least as safe a bet as the most eagle-eyed vigilance. And this goes for avoidance of anything in the material cosmos from the smallest stone to the largest star.

If, then, we are intrinsically too clumsy to dodge meteorites, may we not at least look the rascals in the eye and take a reading on our fate? What have these rare captives to say for themselves? Can we curry a clue from our battle-scarred prisoners of war?

Although meteorites, like hailstones, often show fluted surfaces and sometimes a cone or other symmetrical shape suggesting a stable attitude in flight through the air, this superficial feature bears little relation to their basic structure. Chemically they are usually classified in three main divisions: irons, stones and stony-irons which are sponge-shaped alloys with rocky matter in the holes that may be the stuff all planets grew from.

All of the largest-known meteorites (the Hoba West, the three brought by Peary from Cape York in Greenland, the 16-ton Willamette of Oregon, the 27-ton Bacubirito and other great ones in Mexico and elsewhere) are irons, apparently because only such dense metal is tough enough in large mass to sustain the shock and heat of earthly arrival. The typical meteoric alloy of 91 percent iron, 8 percent nickel, 1 percent cobalt and minor materials gives a strong hint of the deep interior of the earth if one can accept the theory that these are truly the shattered bones of a sister planet.

The stony meteorites are much more numerous but smaller and harder to find or recognize. The biggest stone ever known to have landed intact (in Arkansas) weighs 750 pounds. Another, of which more than three thousand exploded fragments have been recovered (in Kansas), has an aggregate weight of 1,325 pounds. Their almost unclassifiable varieties can be roughly divided into chondrites and achondrites, the former consisting of hard, rounded, hail-like chondrules with proportions of metallic elements closely matching those found in the sun and weakly cemented into conglomerate masses of olivine, bronzite, feldspar, etc., while the latter are even more varied and crumbly mixtures dominated by silicates, sulfides and limestones.

Dr. Harold C. Urey, astrochemist, says, "The structure of the chondrites suggests that they were formed during very large-scale storms as might be expected" in the "turbulent . . . convection cells" of a "protoplanet" about 100,000 miles in diameter. His detailed reasoning as to the "characteristic structure of the chondrules," which "must have accumulated into larger bodies together with cementing material," been "broken by collisions, assembled into large and small objects, and the process repeated," fits in rather nicely with evidence that the crystalline patterns of iron meteorites and occasional traces of diamonds found in some of them could have been formed only under the conditions of enormous pressure and heat that would exist in the interior of a good-sized planet. The average age of meteoritic metal of between four and five billion years, as determined by radio-activity, is also consistent with the generally accepted age of the solar system.

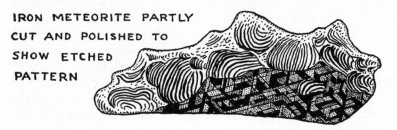

IRON METEORITE PARTLY
CUT AND POLISHED TO
SHOW ETCHED
PATTERN

"On detailed microscopic examination," according to physicist S. Fred Singer, "metallurgists can even see in the meteorites evidences of the sudden release of pressure, presumably due to an explosive collision, which disintegrated the planet. The signs are certain distortions in the crystal structure and sudden transformations of phase in the content of the iron-nickel alloy."

Even the mysterious class of glassy meteorities known as tektites, which no man has ever reported seeing fall from the sky, has recently been associated with the shattered-planet hypothesis. Made of semitransparent greenish-black silicate "fairly similar to obsidian," these curious flight-folded blobs have been found by the millions over various parts of the earth from Bohemia to Australia. They may well be the "ancient black stones" that mystified Antoine de Saint-Exupéry while wandering upon his inaccessible virgin plateau of minute sea shells in the Sahara. Although widely considered as molten earthy "drops" of splash after a major meteoritic collision with the earth or possibly splash from a similar crash on the moon or maybe even from a comet impact, none of these theories has explained all the evidence, so it is just possible they may yet prove to be fine spray from the low-density surface of the missing planet flung outward when it exploded, a tiny percentage of it eons later to come to Earth.

The major debris from this postulated planet-crash — or whatever kind of dissolution it was — is still strewn capriciously all the way around the sun and, together with other jetsam (evidently from comets), forms a vast wreath of meteoric streams, some of which regularly encounter the earth on her yearly rounds. So we have the Perseid meteor showers every August 11, the fiery streaks seeming to radiate out of the constellation of Perseus, the Orionids out of Orion about October 22, the Taurids from Taurus on November 9, the Leonids November 15, the Andromedes around November 20, the Geminids December 11, and so on — the intensity of each shower varying from year to year according to the density of the stream where the earth rolls through it. More than six hundred such streams have been identified, some (like the Perseids) moving almost perpendicular to the earth's orbit, some (like the Andromedes) barely overtaking us in a nearly parallel course, and some (like the Leonids) moving in a contrary direction to hit the earth head on at a combined approach speed of 44 miles a second.

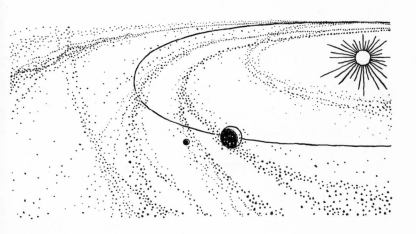

Although the vast majority of these currents are much too far away to encounter the earth at all, it is not hard to see that their average plane makes an angle of only 3° with the earth's orbit and that they form a sort of brim around the sun — not as definite or thin or smoothly circular as the rings of Saturn but more lens-shaped, thicker than the solar diameter in places, unevenly elliptical and rippling as in a breeze. This ecliptic halo is just visible, even with the naked eye, above the hidden sun on a clear moonless night, especially in low latitudes shortly after twilight in late winter or before dawn in the fall. Known as the zodiacal light (or *Gegenschein* where opposite the sun), it is a delicate wedge-shaped solar glow (about 15° wide at the horizon and tapering upward some 30°) reflected off the quadrillions of tiny grains flowing like bullets of dust about the sun, and which, according to one calculation, would be numerous enough to account for the light even if none of the motes were larger than ⅕₅ of an inch in diameter or less than five miles apart.

That there is more than dust or small particles involved in these streams, however, is evident from the fact that so many of their orbits have been found to match the orbits of comets. First

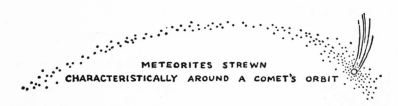

METEORITES STREWN CHARACTERISTICALLY AROUND A COMET'S ORBIT

proof of a cometary-meteoric bond came in 1865 when H. A. Newton and later G. V. Schiaparelli tracked down the course of Tuttle's comet of 1862 to the exact trail of the Perseids. When Temple's comet in 1866 turned out to be following the path of the Leonids, Encke's that of the Taurids, Halley's the Aquarids, Biela's the Andromedes, etc., the last lingering doubts disappeared.

Then in 1885, near the end of the annual Andromede shower, on the evening of November 27, during which three trained observers estimated they saw "forty thousand meteors in four hours," an average of nearly three per second, an eight-pound chunk of meteoric iron landed near Mazapil, Mexico, at 9 P.M. This

astronomers have confidently accepted as "a piece of Biela's comet," probably the first cometary fragment ever examined by man. Scientists have since learned about such huge meteoric evidences as the ¾-mile-wide, 500-feet-deep Barringer Crater (some times called Canyon Diablo) near Winslow, Arizona, and recently the two-mile-wide Chubb Crater in northern Quebec. Moreover, these vast holes in the earth's surface have so far failed to provide proof that they were made by any such large solid masses as asteroids, which would seem to be required for them, and, despite extensive drilling and the use of modern detection instruments, nothing unterrestrial of comparable magnitude has been discovered in or near them. The largest meteorite found within six miles of the Arizona crater weighed only half a ton, and the total of hundreds gathered from the 113-square-mile circle inside that radius amounted to but twenty tons.

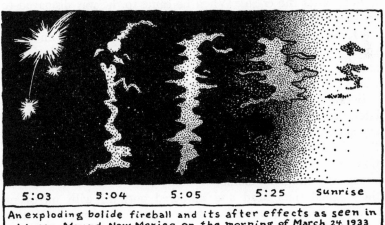

5:03 5:04 5:05 5:25 Sunrise

An exploding bolide fireball and its after effects as seen in Wagon Mound, New Mexico, on the morning of March 24, 1933

On the other hand, something really sensational happened on the morning of June 30, 1908, in central Siberia. Over the vast birch and evergreen forest between the Yenisei and Lena rivers a few hundred miles north of Lake Baikal and the Trans-Siberian Railroad, a tremendous "fiery body" suddenly appeared so high that it was seen 1,000 miles away as it moved swiftly across the sky. The roar was described as "deafening" at 500 miles, and the pressure wave made a sharp peak on the barograph at Kirensk, 300 miles southeast. A Russian in Kansk, 400 miles southwest, reported, "It happened in full daylight. A blue ball half the size of the moon came down — moving fast. It left a bluish wake, stretching for almost its whole course but fading at the end."

Another Russian in a boat on the Angara River, at half the distance saw "a bluish light flash in the north, while from the south came a fiery thing twice as big as the sun, and leaving a wide streak of light behind it."

A peasant sitting on the front steps of his little house in Vanovara, a mere 50 miles south, felt a wave of such heat after the object fell that he thought his clothes would burn. Then as he tried to shield his face with his arms, a sudden invisible blast knocked him off the steps so hard he lost consciousness. This was presumably the shock wave of impact arriving about four minutes after the crash. When he came to, he was dismayed to see that his house had collapsed.

Meanwhile, 350 miles farther south, a train made an emergency stop because of "earth tremors." And next day a herd of 1500 reindeer was found dead north of Vanovara in a region where all the trees were leaning away from the blast center.

Because of the inaccessibility of this swampy region and the later confusion of war and revolution, it was 1928 before an expedition was sent out under Professor L. A. Kulik of the Russian Academy of Sciences to make an on-the-spot investigation. Professor Kulik at length reported that he found an area about fifty miles in diameter "completely devastated" with all the original trees dead and uprooted outward with increasing severity, from one point "as if by a giant blowtorch." Within a mile of this center he counted about two hundred separate craters ranging up to 150 feet in diameter. Although he did not succeed in digging out any meteoric fragments because of the water that flowed into every hole, he estimated that the total weight of the pieces might be "around forty thousand tons."

Astronomers had already decided the phenomenon must have been connected with the annual Pons-Winneckeid meteor shower of June 29 and they easily verified the further significant fact that the Pons-Winnecke comet on its six-year orbit was only three million miles (a thirtieth of the solar distance) from the earth at the time of the crash. That, I think, is the second closest that the earth has come to the nucleus of any comet in modern history. In any case, it seems more likely that the 1908 fireball was an offshoot of the comet than a stray hunk of antimatter (page 486) as has been recently proposed. And if so, it provides in turn a strong clue as to what comets are made of.

Until modern times, no one knew how far away comets were or what they signified, and the dramatic tails of these rare and unpredictable visitations understandably were feared as omens of tragedy and associated with occultism and the beards of prophets. The very word "comet" came from the Greek *kometes*, "the long-haired one," and its appearance symbolized the mystery of flowing locks which, half-revealing, half-concealing, fascinated more than they enlightened. Had not a bushy-tailed comet foretold the death of Caesar? And another that of Vespasian even while he denied it, saying it couldn't mean him since it was hairy and he was bald?

It seems to have appeared fairly plausible in those days that comets were really disembodied spirits of some unusual kind. Certainly they had a sort of mental quality not unlike thoughts moving among the stars. Whence came they? And whither did they go? No man could say. But if one had an open mind, one could learn from them to mark well each fleeting thought, to inscribe it deep in memory so it might eventually be turned to account. For once a thought is beyond one's ken, how can one foreknow its return? Like a comet its orbit is unknown, perhaps hyperbolic. Perhaps it is harnessed to some foreign star. Or perhaps it just travels straight and free and — who knows — may be utterly powerless ever to regain this world of sense.

Despite many such broad and a few quite reasonable ideas on comets taught by early Greek philosophers, Aristotle, the famous chronicler of old wives' tales on meteorology, maintained comets were actually nothing but "exhalations from the earth to the upper atmosphere." And his view prevailed throughout most of the world for fifteen centuries. Even Ptolemy's great *Almagest* did not classify comets as heavenly bodies. And when a bright one appeared in 1456, the Church, unable to understand it, could only pray indiscriminately, "Protect us, O Lord, from Satan, the Turks, and the Comet."

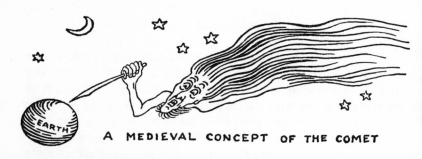

A MEDIEVAL CONCEPT OF THE COMET

A typical description of the great comet of 1528 by an awed observer said it looked "so horrible and produced such great terror in the common people that some died of fear and others fell sick. It appeared to be of excessive length and was the color of blood. At its summit rose the figure of a bent arm, holding in its hand a great scimitar as if about to strike. Three stars quivered near the tip of the blade. On both sides of the rays of this comet there appeared a great number of axes, knives and blood-drenched swords, among which were many hideous slowly-shifting faces with beards and bristling hair."

It was methodical Tycho Brahe at Uraniborg who first penetrated the mystery of comets with some solid fact. Comparing his
own precise observations of a comet in 1577 with observations
made at Prague, he calculated the comet's parallax accurately
enough to prove it was "at least six times as far away as the
moon," and at some points so much farther away than at other
points that it must have passed right through the "spheres" of
the planetary orbits, casting serious doubt upon their presumed
rigidity.

Yet although this evidence may at last have convinced people
that comets had nothing to do with lightning or weather, it did
not diminish "the wholesome moral effect" the comet of 1662
had in Boston in warning the populace to abstain from "volup-
tuousness and abuse of the good creatures of God by licentious-
ness in drinking and fashions in apparel" — an accomplishment
that might well require an atomic missile today. Indeed, it was
only after Edmund Halley, the second Astronomer Royal of
England, noticed a striking similarity in the recorded paths of the
comets of 1456, 1531, 1607 and 1682, that the comet figure
noticeably started its decline from Olympus. For Halley was
the first to establish that comets, like planets, were amenable to
Newton's new law of gravitation, and he became so convinced
that the comets of 1456, 1531, 1607 and 1682 were really
the same one swooping around and around the sun that he
confidently predicted *the* comet's return about the end of 1758 or
early in 1759. In doing so, he correctly attributed the
disparity between its last two periods to the gravitational influence of Jupiter, who, passing close to the comet during its
earlier round, had delayed it more than a year.

Halley himself could not live long enough to see his comet
return, but his prediction is a classic in astronomy, and observers all over Europe reached an unprecedented pitch of excitement in 1758, the first year in history when a comet was
definitely expected. And sure enough, an amateur named

Palitzsch spotted the faithful visitor on Christmas night, and within a month hundreds of astronomers were jealously measuring it as it drew near, reaching perihelion on March 12, 1759.

This dramatic triumph of human science naturally stimulated a flurry of comet hunters in the succeeding years, among whom none was more ardent than Charles Messier, the assistant director of the Paris Observatory, who tirelessly combed everything in the visible heavens with his telescopes, particularly the promising western sky after nightfall and the east before dawn, inadvertently stumbling upon and recording a number of mysterious "'fuzzy stars" that looked tantalizingly like tailless comets except that they would not move. Of course, there was no one to tell Messier that most of these nebulous annoyances would ultimately prove to be very remote "island universes," each big enough to contain far more stars and comets than all he had ever heard of. Instead, his single-minded passion carried him to such lengths of comet concentration that his compatriot La Harpe needed but one anecdote to engrave his personality forever into the annals of astronomy. "Messier is a very worthy man," wrote La Harpe, "and has the simplicity of a baby. Some years ago he lost his wife, and his final attentions to her prevented him from discovering a comet he was on the search for, and which Montaigne of Limoges got away from him. He was in despair. When a friend condoled with him on his loss he replied, with his head full of the comet, 'Oh dear! to think that when I had discovered twelve, this Montaigne should have got my thirteenth,' and his eyes filled with tears until, remembering what it was he ought to be weeping for, he moaned, 'Oh, my poor wife!' but went on crying for his comet."

In the last two centuries astronomers, tracking back through the earlier circuits of Halley's celestial roundsman, have identified it as early as 240 B.C. and discovered it is none other than the famous comet of A.D. 66 that announced the fall of Jerusalem, provoking Josephus to inquire: "What shall we say to the comet that hung over Jerusalem for one whole year together, in the figure of the sword?" It is also woven into the Bayeux tapestry as the bearded star of 1066 that foretold the Norman Conquest. On its twenty-eighth recorded visit in 1835 it came just in time to officiate over the birth of Mark Twain who, seeing "my comet" back again on April 20, 1910, in his seventy-fifth year, rightfully concluded that he had rounded out his own allotted orbit and, next evening at 6:30, passed away — followed in due course by the comet.

But if Halley's is the best-known comet, its significance pales before the growing multitude of others, some half-dozen of which turn up annually, a good two thirds of them apparently never having been seen on Earth before. Although it is not easy to keep track of comets, whose heads, tails and even orbits are notoriously variable, about four hundred were recorded by naked eye before Galileo's day, and now the orbits of more than a thousand have been carefully plotted and sorted. These are of an amazing variety, ranging from the conservative Schwassmann-Wachmann comet discovered in 1927 swinging around its orbit that is more nearly circular than Mercury's and lies wholly between the paths of Jupiter and Saturn, to such wild ones as the great dagger-shaped apparition of 1843, which missed hitting the sun by a narrower margin than any yet known.

As described by Charles G. Abbot of the Smithsonian Observatory, the latter

blazed out suddenly in full daylight on February 28, 1843. It was seen simultaneously in Mexico, the United States and southern Europe. On the steamer *Owen Glendower*, off the Cape of Good Hope, the passengers were surprised to see a short, dagger-like object following the sun toward the western horizon. The head of the comet was then situated only 1°23′, or little more than twice the sun's diameter, from the center of the sun itself, and observers in Italy were able to trace the tail four or five degrees at midday. On March 3 the tail measured 25° and on March 11 a second tail, twice as long as the first, shot out in a single day. The Russian, Boguslawski, estimated the length of tail at 581 million miles on March 21, or longer than the radius of Jupiter's orbit. When the comet went closest to the sun, its center was but 78,000 miles outside the sun's surface (a third of the distance between earth and moon). The comet went right around the sun through 180° of its path in 2 hours 11 minutes at the rate of 366 miles a second.

The general conclusion of the study of cometary orbits to date is that probably all of them are elliptical, indicating that comets circulate entirely within the solar system and are not, in any known case, strangers passing through from outside. Even though a few of their orbits have been plotted as parabolic or slightly hyperbolic where near the sun, this is likely due to the perturbations of Jupiter and other local warpings of a closed over-all course. For comets are very susceptible to gravitational influences.

The latter observation, long since confirmed, is naturally a strong indication that, despite their spectacular appearance, comets are surprisingly light in mass. The gaudy one that swooped among Jupiter's moons in 1889 without distracting a single little satellite from its accustomed beat is a good illustration of this lightness, for only the blustering comet itself was lured off its route. And three years earlier Brooks' comet in 1886 had been literally "thrown for a loop" by Jupiter when its swipe at the jovial giant summarily reduced its own period from 29 to 7 years.

About seventy comets, it turns out, actually have orbits so closely tied to Jupiter's that they are spoken of as members of his family. These all go around the sun in the same direction as the planets, their aphelions close to the Jovian circuit and their periods averaging a little more than half his year. And theory suggests that all these filial bodies originally enjoyed much larger orbits and longer years until as chance perturbations brought their perihelions closer to Jupiter, one by one he captured those that moved most nearly parallel to himself, progressively bending their paths toward the sun and shortening their years. Encke's comet, for instance, the first of the family to be recognized, in 1819, now has the tightest-known cometary orbit of three and a third years and therefore is a good bet to be the oldest current member.

But Jupiter is not the only planet to have captured a covey of comets. Similar if smaller families are attributable to Saturn, Uranus and Neptune, who, one can surmise, will pass some of these thralls slowly inward from household to household like wayward orphans until they finally waste away. Halley's comet, for example, probably a relative newcomer to planetary circles, is now considered a member of Neptune's clan and, having a retrograde orbit, should offer stubborn resistance to capture by Uranus or any other forward-revolving body. Almost half the outer comets, however, drifting apparently at random, have been found to be flowing in the general direction of the planetary tide and are ultimate candidates for the Jovian mill, the rest revolving, if not withershins, at least at some wide angle off the ecliptic plane. Their average orbital period has been estimated by A. C. D. Crommelin, the British authority, as a leisurely 40,000 years.

Biela's comet breaking in two 1846

A different and closer kind of cometary grouping is that exemplified by Biela's comet, a member of Jupiter's family with a six-and-a-half-year orbit. Upon its third observed return, in 1846, a strange protuberance appeared on its glowing head. Then, in plain view of the astronomers, the comet broke into two parts which moved off into the distance, steadily increasing the gap between them. In 1852 the pieces reappeared, swinging back around the sun one and a half million miles apart.

But something even more drastic happened to the great September comet of 1882. Plainly visible in full daylight, it swooped through the sun's corona only 300,000 miles from the white-hot surface at better than a million miles an hour, its head being violently disrupted by the huge tides raised by the closeness of the sun. And the disruption almost immediately became a split, whereupon each nuclear half split again like generating amoebae, resulting in four sections which spread out in the direction of the departing motion. Although this comet had not been a member of any known planetary family, astronomers soon calculated from the four new slightly diverging orbits that the separate quarters will "return as four comets" of a new group between the twenty-fifth and twenty-eighth centuries.

A later reverse calculation into the past was no less fruitful in showing that the five great comets of 1668, 1843, 1880, 1882 and 1887, all of which narrowly missed the sun on strikingly similar orbits, were almost certainly once parts of a single great comet which, in a previous gyration, also burst asunder from the strain of a close shave with the sun.

Thus we have a trend in comets, an apparent tendency to evolve not only by being drawn toward the sun like moths to a flame, but by successive solar tidal disintegrations. Whether many of the constituent cometary parts ever recombine in the lazy outer reaches beyond Pluto is unknown, but at least the solid meteoric components seem to sieve out and gravitate toward the sun. Ever since the separating halves of Biela's comet were last seen in 1852, no gaseous glow has reappeared, but rather a new swarm of meteors has turned up on Biela's old orbit, and these have continued to encounter the earth every November as the aforementioned Andromedes, just as the disappearance of Temple's comet produced the Leonids, and so on. And all these sundry vagabonds of the void seem to keep spiraling "downward" like hail toward the sun at a very slow but calculable rate which Harold Urey says should pull in every grain and stone up to six inches in diameter from as far out as the asteroidal zone within three billion years.

What mainly distinguishes the comets from meteoric and larger solid bodies of course is their extremely low density, an unmistakable sign of their gassy nature. For if the denser debris of the sky derives largely from the grinding of the iron inner planets, the giddy comets are just as surely mere scraps of flatulent superfluity somehow unassimilated by the turgid outer planets.

The spectra of comets, indeed, shows them to consist largely of compounds of the common gases hydrogen, nitrogen and oxygen, with carbon and bits of such metals as sodium, iron, nickel and chromium — the preponderant stuff of the outer giants. Ever since the great comet of 1882 passed between sun and Earth, turning completely invisible to the biggest telescopes as viewed against the solar disk, we have known that a comet may contain no solid nucleus of observable size, no opaque lumps much beyond meteoric dimensions.

The leading comet model is Whipple's carefully reasoned swarm of methane, ammonia and water molecules that freeze in outer space and, mixed with metallic dusts, tend to stick together as snow crystals, flakes and ultimately (after hundreds of millions of years) huge "gritty snowballs" as big as asteroids. There are "probably some twenty billion" of these curious conglomerations, according to astrophysicist George Gamow, "moving mostly far beyond the orbit of Pluto within a sphere about three light years in diameter." Gamow estimates their average weight as around ten billion tons, which is astronomically quite insignificant and would bring the total mass of all the comets to less than a thirtieth part of the earth.

Obviously there is much less than one chance in a million that any given member of this immense reservoir of meandering snowballs will get seduced into the planetary regions in our lifetime, and those seen looping around the sun are as rare as albino butterflies at a masthead lantern. They also must have undergone a dramatic chemical change as they approached this inner region. For when the solar heat melts a comet's outer surfaces, the body sizzles like pork in a flame. It starts to fuss and fume and its grit to fritter away into the expanding clouds of glowing gas. Layer after layer of the frozen methane and ammonia and finally plain water ice is aroused from hibernation and the crystallized nucleus softens and evaporates into the growing luminescent coma that may pulse or flare, according to the little-understood combinations of its elements, sometimes briefly exceeding the sun in volume and, as it draws within the asteroidal zone, usually shooting out a spectacular tail.

In 1909, to cite a not-untypical case, Halley's comet had a coma measured as 14,000 miles in diameter when it got to within three times the earth's distance from the sun, and its tail was scarcely a bud. By the time it was only twice as far away as the earth, the coma had swelled to 220,000 miles across, and the tail was reaching out for scores of millions of miles. At perihelion (inside Venus' orbit) the coma had shrunk to 120,000 miles again, while the tail exceeded 100 million miles; then in passing the earth's orbit on departure the coma surprisingly puffed way up to 320,-000 miles!

Some of this variability may be accounted for by such free radicals (page 89) as imine (NH), hydroxyl (OH), methylene (CH_2), which are stable at very low temperatures as must exist in a comet much beyond Pluto but which become explosively reactive as soon as they are heated a few tens of degrees above absolute zero. According to a recent suggestion by Bertram Donn and Urey, the explosion of thawing radicals may be damped for a while in a sun-bound comet by their dilution in an overwhelming mass of stable molecules. But as the rising heat evaporates the stable material, the radicals will become more and more concentrated until some outside trigger of energy like a solar ion or a cosmic ray sets off a "chain-reacting explosion" which must "continue until it runs into a large concentration of stable molecules or of meteoric material in the ice." Then the comet can subside again.

The initial mystery of the tail is only slightly more easily solved. As one astonished observer of the comet of 1843 pointed out, when the head completed a semicircle around the sun in two hours and eleven minutes, the 580,000,000-mile tail also swept around, always streaming away from the sun, its tip "traveling" more than 1,800,000,000 miles in 131 minutes at about 230,000 miles a second — which would be exceeding the speed of light! The answer, first intimated in the seventeenth century by Hooke but not generally understood even in the nineteenth, is that a comet's tail does not remain the same tail any more than a stream of water from a hose remains the same water. The modern evidence is that it is composed of flowing components of very thin gas and probably particles of fine dust (less than 1/100,000th of an inch in diameter) that are continuously shot away from the comet's head by the added impact of sunlight and solar ions upon the coma's vacillating chemical pressures.

Although these submicroscopic particles are naturally attracted by the sun, it has been found that "upon a molecule of gas which absorbs its radiation, the solar pressure may exceed the solar attraction as much as 150 times." Also a 100-foot balloon in space will be blown out of its orbit by the solar wind at rates up to 3.7 miles per day. A comet thus wastes away in the manner of a burning candle, its luminous "smoke" dispersing never to return, its nuclear "wick" (probably containing many such meteoric lumps as landed in Siberia in 1908) giving its gassy head a stable center of gravity.

Although some comets do not show any tail at all, at least nine out of ten begin to sprout one when they reach the region of the inner planets, and the tail is likely to be well developed by the time they swing inside the earth's orbit. It may be bushy or bobbed or fan-shaped and often forms some sort of hollow cone or flamelike envelope which is certain to be constantly changing, occasionally even flickering — perhaps partly under the influence of

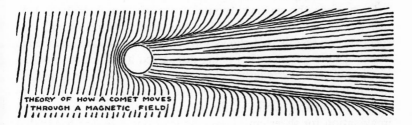

THEORY OF HOW A COMET MOVES THROUGH A MAGNETIC FIELD

passing magnetic gradients. Sometimes a second or third tail will appear near perihelion. Borelli's comet in 1903 sported nine at its climax, and Morehouse's in 1908 dropped one tail only to grow a complete new one two days later.

In any case, all the evidence shows that comet tails, directly or indirectly, are fleeting gifts of the sun which, like roses or maidens, bloom today but should not be expected to look the same tomorrow. You can actually see the streams of luminous ions jetting forth from the fluorescent gas of the coma like strange slow flames, their divergent initial courses ultimately curving downstream together in blended obedience to the powerful pressure of the sun — downstream being characteristically away from the sun regardless of which way the comet is moving, so that a receding comet lets its tail blow ahead of it like a freight train's smoke before a following gale.

Even when the separate spouts of a single comet make it look like a fish with graceful curving fins and translucent tail, the spectroscope reveals that the various caudal streams are really composed of different elements being discharged at different velocities like jets of several strengths coming from the same hose nozzle. It may in fact be the sparseness of comet gases that makes this multi-discharge possible while at the same time the tails defy human imagination for sheer emptiness. At least one estimate has it that 2,000 cubic miles of comet tail contain less matter than a cubic inch of ordinary air. Which, if true, should enable almost any schoolboy to heft a real comet tail, if only he could manage a grip on one.

Following through with the concept that the comet tail serves as the smoke from a candle, we find that once a comet falls into the gay debauchery of swooping around the sun with a flashy tail, its days are numbered. Even though its frozen inner nucleus may still be fairly well insulated from the solar heat by many coats of dust (as theorized by Whipple), the mad indulgence can permit it only a few dozen or, at most, a few hundred passes at the sun before it is completely disintegrated into its meteoric components like Biela's and other obviously dying comets. Of course it may kick and spit and flare up a few times, as did Schwassmann-Wachmann's perennial comet that brightened a hundredfold in four days of 1934. Few of them, however, can hope to escape so successfully as did Lexell's will-o'-the-wisp in 1770 after making the closest observed approach to the earth of any comet in history — one and a half million miles — only to fail to show up on its next scheduled return in 1776, having declared its own independence in the appropriate "spirit of '76" after a sharp orbital clash against the tyranny of Jupiter.

ACCRETION AXIS OF SUN - WHERE POOL OF COMETS IS REPLENISHED

The depletion of comets, of course, takes into consideration only the outflow of the comet reservoir. R. A. Lyttleton of Cambridge University feels sure the reservoir must also have some

sort of an inflow — an accretion of source material that, he postu-
lates, is likely to be the galactic clouds of dust and gas that are
strewn more or less invisibly among the stars. The sun presumably
plows through this raw material off and on and, according to
Lyttleton's calculations, must pick up a certain amount of it by
gravitational attraction, particularly along an "accretion axis" in
the solar wake where centers of density in the irregular inward
flow of captured cloud molecules gradually thicken and knot into
comets.

Whatever their actual evolution, these celestial fireflies are not
only the most spectacular of visitors in the sky but perhaps they
may yet justify, to a greater extent than we now realize, some
of the ancient apprehensions as to their ultimate danger for the
earth. Indeed, if the Pons-Winnecke comet spat out the Siberian
fireball in 1908 from three million miles away, just think what
Biela's comet *might* have produced when it brushed within a
20,000-mile whisker of the earth's orbit a bare month ahead of us
in 1832. If it had chanced to come a few weeks later, could not
a hundred Barringer and Chubb craters have resulted, perhaps
wiping out whole towns or cities with the impacts of the comet's
still-frozen nuclei, later melting away to a mere trace of metal as
in Arizona? The greater grow the cities of earth and the denser
her population, the surer must occasional disaster come from this
source. How would a trigger-itchy dictator with atomic arsenal
react even today to an unidentified object descending from the
general azimuth of his potential enemy and exploding upon his
capital with catastrophic violence?

Certainly man in his material lowliness can neither predict nor
prevent such an empyrean provocation nor stem the will of God.
Nor can he descry what unsuspected breeds of cosmic gadflies
may yet arrive at any moment out of the black reaches of space
with motive unknown to sting the tender, and ever-tenderer,
flesh of Earth.

6. introduction to the sun

COME UP HERE WITH ME if you would meet the ancient father of our world. "Come," as Empedocles said in Agrigentum in 450 B.C., "and I shall tell thee first of all the beginning of the sun, and the sources from which have sprung all the things we now behold — the earth and the billowy sea, the damp vapor and the titan air that binds his circle fast round all things."

There may be some people living down on Earth, even in habitually sunny lands, who manage to take our nearest star, the sun, for granted. But to most humans I think El Sol is so closely tied to their moods and emotions, if not their health, that he is in large degree the very spunk and soul of the world — literally the light of life on Earth.

Even to say that our home globe is a floating speck of ash that reflects a minim of solar glory is almost a cosmological exaggeration, so great is his bulk and brilliance compared to the earth's: his volume one and a third million times larger, his brightness that of a perpetual hydrogen-bomb burst 865,000 miles in diameter that radiates some hundred thousand *tons* of light per second.

SACRIFICING TO RA, THE SUN GOD IN ANCIENT EGYPT

Yes, light has weight and can be measured in tons, as we shall presently see. And the ancient intuitive understanding of this now proven fact may be a contributing factor in the almost universal early deification of the sun as a god: great Ra of the Egyptians, bright Mithras of the Persians, beautiful Apollo of the Greeks, and other blazing deities from China to Parthia to Stonehenge to the Inca "children of the sun" in Peru. Indeed, with great justification have these man-projected solar personalities held sway over our pristine superstitions for unnumbered eons, even as the living sun has lorded it over the phoenix earth — our pulsing world that was born of brimstone, suckled in the whirling maelstrom of planetary motion, raised from fire to ashes to smoke to gas to liquid to solid to fusion to fission to fire . . .

Yet the sun is benign as well as overwhelming. Ever since he incubated the molecules of organic birth, the sun has had a wonderful and direct effect on life, showing a quality that is mysterious and indefinable but nonetheless real. Even before he taught seaweed to be a tree he was godfather to all the creatures of the deep, and later to the buzzing insects, the beasts, the birds. I hear that the cages where falcons are quartered traditionally face to the east because "the morning sun is very beneficial" to them, especially to the small and beautiful kestrel, embodiment of Osiris or Aurora, whose burnished plumage flashes rubies of light caught from the sun. And it is said the Arctic tern loves the daylight so much he will fly with the summer from pole to pole so that the sun almost never sets from his sight.

Perhaps it is for the same reason that when a man feels weary or depressed or in pain, just stepping into clear sunshine does something to him. I have felt it often. Sunshine is manifestly more than heat and light and invisible rays — even as the whole can be greater than the sum of its parts. It is something subtler, nearer to the spiritual, something close to the quick of life itself. It seems to me that the sun has in some degree the quality of a patriarchal blessing — a bestowal of that special feeling of security that comes through the love of dear parents still living in the old family homestead where one was born and raised. For the sun is verily the birthstead of the whole earth, and the warmth of human blood is as surely our heritage from him as the salty savor of

THE SUN'S-EYE VIEW OF WESTERN EUROPE - SEASON BY SEASON

our sweat and tears was given us by the briny ocean where our flippered ancestors swam and loved and died some three hundred million years ago. The terrestrial seasons *are* his very gaze — summer made by his straight-down stare, winter decreed where he looks askance, spring and autumn at angles between. Even the growing perspectives of our minds may come more from his influence than we know, as all days are parts of the same day in the eyes of the great one who shines continuously on the other side of the darkest night. Indeed where the sun looks it is ever day and "time" itself stands still and clocks strike only noon, noon, noon as the twilight vanishes before his face.

Knowing the glory of this parental star of our world, through modern science as well as personal adventure, it is easy to understand the degree to which the sun still impresses primitive peoples. Could any college-trained orator be more eloquent than the South Sea chieftain who, gazing at the sun, exclaimed in his pidgin English: "Me lookum old big fella fire. He high up too much. He alla same one fella island. He fly long long. He no come down."

Almost the very opposite of such a hypocorism was Epicurus' surprising estimate in 300 B.C. that the sun might be "two feet in diameter." If this idea seems inexplicable for a renowned Greek philosopher and physicist, remember that some Eskimos today still believe that when the sun sets in the western ocean he is paddled by kayak back to the eastern horizon at night just beyond the northern skyline, thus accounting also for the northern lights of their region.

If you put your imagination in the primitive circumstance of living on a flat earth where the sky is nothing but a magic ceiling inhabited by mysterious supernatural actors in an endless drama, you can appreciate the difficulty of being factual about the size and height of the sun. And so the achievement of Anaxagoras in calculating the sun to be "a great hot stone" as large as the Peloponnesus not only startled the court of Pericles but caused the eminent philosopher himself to be exiled for blasphemy. Yet Anaxagoras had come remarkably close to the right dimension if we allow him the assumption of a flat earth. For he had measured the angle of the sun's altitude as seen from widely different places and had figured its distance by triangulation or parallax as 4,000 miles, which is nearly the earth's actual radius and, had it really been the sun's height over a flat earth, would have given Anaxagoras just such a solar parallax as he actually measured.

Aristarchos of Samos, the astronomer, later timed the half-moon periods as accurately as he could without a telescope and concluded that the sun was "twenty times as far away as the moon," but it remained for Poseidonius, of all the ancients, to come closest to the right distance figures for both the moon and sun: 208,000 and 70,000,000 miles respectively. Both estimates are less than 25 percent too low, which is indeed impressive in view of the fact that Poseidonius was only timing eclipses and measuring shadows on the moon and earth without a telescope, and probably with no instrument more advanced than a homemade measuring stick or a diopter (primitive theodolite).

Only in the age of modern astronomy opened by Copernicus and Tycho have we come to realize that the sun is not really "on fire" in the familiar combustive sense and that, as some engineer recently figured out, if the sun were made of coal burning in oxygen he could not have stayed alight for more than 2,500 years. Quite plainly, something much more profound and basic than fire is blazing in that patriarch of worlds in our corner of the Milky Way. Yet even the relatively enlightened theories of eighteenth- and nineteenth-century astronomers could hardly have gotten below the surface of the solar mystery while the anatomy of the atom was still unknown, for the secrets of stars and of atoms have repeatedly turned out to be essentially the same secret, and, as we will presently see, there is a common flesh to all matter and the simplest of keys may fit locks of widely different make.

Looking at the sun through a smoked glass, one is apt to think of him as a simple sphere of definite size — a visible size which by strange coincidence so closely matches the moon's apparent dimensions that in some solar eclipses (when the moon is at her nearest to the earth) the moon more than covers the sun's disk while in others (when the moon can be 14 percent farther away) she doesn't quite do so and leaves a thin ring of direct sunlight showing completely around her. This coincidence is almost duplicated in the fact that both sun and moon rotate in the same period: about 27 days. Yet the sun is far from being a simple sphere and not only turns much faster at his equator than his poles but actually has as many sizes as he has layers, all of which are gaseous and, with one exception, normally invisible.

The surface of the sun that we see as brilliant light is known to astronomers as the photosphere, from *photos*, the Greek for light. Magnified through a modern spectroheliogram, it has a fibrous woolly look in hydrogen light and a cerebral or breadfruity appearance in the light of calcium, and in almost any kind of filtered photograph it looks strongly granulated. Yet surprisingly, although these sun grains turn out to have diameters ranging from about 180 to 1,000 miles, each grain lasts only a few minutes. This effect was described by the papal astronomer Secchi a hun-

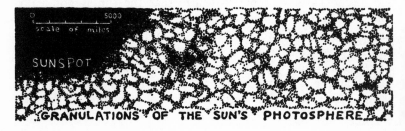

GRANULATIONS OF THE SUN'S PHOTOSPHERE

dred years ago as resembling "grains of rice bubbling in a milky fluid," but lately his rice pudding has been deduced to be really composed of fountains of hot gases that continuously jet upward from deeper layers until they cool off and fall back like bubbles in a boiling cauldron.

The flaming visible surface appears to have a certain solidity just because it maintains its average size, shape and pattern, yet it is really a thousand times more vacuous than a candle-flame on Earth, and even the concentrated moiling gases hidden a thousand miles below it are a hundred times thinner than earthly air. From there on down into the deep heart of the sun, however, the pressure and density increase steadily, reaching the compactness of water about halfway, and in the center itself the highly compressed gassy matter is ten times as dense as steel, the pressure 100 billion times that of earthly air at sea level and the temperature something like 40,000,000° F.

Thus the sun's body is extremely variable and, although nothing but gas, the gas is inconceivably hard, hot and heavy at the center and nearly as unimaginably complex and dynamic in its massive turbulence, especially toward the outer and more volatile layers. In fact, it has been possible for man to deduce and to measure the sun's awesome activity only because the extreme heat and pressure of the solar interior break down all material elements into relatively simple masses of protons, electrons, alpha particles, and so on, while the spectacular chromosphere and corona layers outside the photosphere, though normally invisible because of the photospheric glare, can be plainly seen and photographed when the photosphere is blocked off as in a total eclipse.

The general solar circulation, as now accepted by most astrophysicists, adds up to a whirling interchange of elementary particles caught between the twin pressures of heat from within and weight from without, complicated by the sun's aforementioned nonuniform rotation and focused around magnetic hurricanes thousands of miles in diameter that are but eddies of much greater magnetic tides (sometimes called magneto-hydrodynamic waves) extending probably all the way through the sun and out the other side.

These hurricanes, commonly known on Earth as sunspots, were

once described as "flying birds upon the sun" by an ancient Chinese stargazer who must have spotted some extra-large ones which can be plainly visible to the eye without magnification through smoke or sunset haze. But they are now recognized to influence the earth in more ways than the high priests of the Middle Kingdom could possibly have divined, being two-way vertical vortices that have no familiar counterpart but behave something as volcanoes might if their active craters were as big as the Pacific Ocean (or up to a hundred times bigger), flaming white-hot and spinning, with violent whirlpools in their centers forming funnels thousands of miles across and sucking deep into them vast masses of incandescent hydrogen at a mile a second. The surrounding parts meanwhile belch out ions of calcium, iron and nickel which are hurled millions of miles upward into the vacuous raging corona on the "top of the sun," where their temperature and speed are rapidly increased a thousandfold before the terrific blast of light and "shock waves" of magnetic forces — the solar wind — that send them out to the planets and far beyond.

If this wild arena of unearthly violence seems terrifying in its magnitude, it is no less awesome in its relentless deliberation. For days in advance, the sunspots' approach is heralded by premonitory increases in radiant heat at the exact points where they are going to erupt, this extra radiation accompanied by the lashing

MAGNETIC LOOP FLARES
ON THE SUN

out of tongues of flame hundreds of thousands of miles high into the corona where they float ominously and literally on the updrafts of sunbeams for hours, sometimes many days. These scarlet streamers are composed of glowing veils of gaseous calcium and often look (in telescopic, time-lapse movies) like bubbles as they billow upward larger and larger, probably following lines of waxing magnetic force which has been measured to increase locally at such periods by more than a thousandfold (up to 4,000 gauss). Sometimes they look like gnarled trees with blazing rain pouring downward from their branches in beautiful magnetic curves that have been clocked at speeds up to 400 miles a second, sometimes like delicate bridges arching from surge to surge, or columns, or odd-shaped flocculi that, though made of a kind of fire, have an ice-bergish propensity for remaining at only 10,000° F. despite the 2,000,000° F. corona all around them.

After a day or two of this weird outer drama, tremendous masses of glowing gas begin to heave on the sun's main surface like budding volcanoes directly under the flaming veils, shortly bursting apart to reveal the open craters we see as sunspots. These look dark because they are relatively much cooler than the rest of the photosphere, which also explains their lower pressure and consequent mawlike action of sucking down hydrogen into their whirling centers like so many celestial bathtub drains. But the most remarkable aspect of their deliberation is the fact that, although at least a few sunspots are nearly always visible, they are far from haphazard. They never appear at the poles and seldom at the equator but always begin close to the sun's 30th parallel of latitude, normally in pairs as in a minuet, a positively charged spot a few degrees of longitude behind a negative spot, often with a corresponding pair charged in the reverse order on the opposite side of the equator. From there they develop slowly and primly as they dance toward the equator with little hope of reaching it, attaining maximum size at about the 20th parallel and normally fading away before they get much beyond the 10th. The life of individual sunspots may thus last anywhere from a few days to several months, only one that I know of having survived as long as a year and a half. But about every eleven years there is a climax of their collective activity, after which their size and numbers decline again only to rise to a new maximum in another ten or twelve years when the order of magnetic polarity of the spots is reversed, the sun's north and south magnetic poles exchanged. The whole 22-year period between similar states of polarity constitutes a complete magnetic cycle.

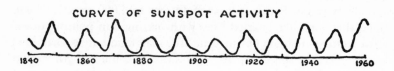

CURVE OF SUNSPOT ACTIVITY

1840   1860   1880   1900   1920   1940   1960

Just why the period averages 22 years and what happens to regulate it are, of course, even harder to deduce in the case of the sun than comparable mysteries inside the earth, but recently astronomers have evolved the now prevailing theory that the magnetic disturbances that regularly develop in the sun may be closely related to his nonuniform spinning. For the great disparity that permits his equatorial day to amount to only 25 Earth days while his polar day lasts for 34 is bound to create latitudinal shear surfaces in the vast, moiling solar gases. These must inevitably influence his magnetic lines of force and, it is believed, mold them into wavy doughnut forms that twist and writhe about his middle latitudes, something like jet streams about the earth, and on both sides of his equator.

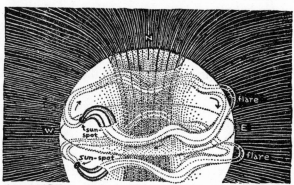

MAGNETIC FIELD PATTERNS OF THE SUN

In any case, since the highly conductive plasma of the sun is material that slides easily parallel to lines of magnetic force but cuts across them only with difficulty, it is understandable that the flow of swirling matter tends to follow the same toroidal lines around the sun — intermittently breaching out of his fiery surface in visible sunspots and spraying ions at thousands of miles a second through his corona to coast to Earth in thirty hours, flowing into Earth's magnetic mantle (the Van Allen belts) and to its magnetic poles, touching off northern and southern lights and rumpling the inner surfaces of the ionosphere. This flow is enough to vibrate all magnetic needles on Earth and disrupt radio communication (which reflects off the ionosphere) and in several known cases to garble telegraph messages and throw power plants out of kilter from Rome to Nome. Such an effect is in addition to the far-reaching influences (on weather and life) of the radiation drop, which, when a big sunspot directly faces the earth, can reduce our share of sunlight by as much as 4 percent.

If it strikes you as hopeless, trying to reckon intelligible cause and effect in this mysterious magnetic and thermal hurly-burly, it may be helpful to know that at least a basic beginning was made some quarter of a century ago in one of the famous early fruits of the atomic age: the theory of the synthesis of helium inside the sun, a masterpiece of astrophysical deduction created by the two German physicists Carl Friedrich von Weizsäcker and Hans A. Bethe. By postulating a complicated but evidently natural sequence of interchanging protons and neutrons among the frenzied nuclei of hydrogen, carbon, nitrogen and oxygen at 40,-000,000° F., they showed how helium is continuously born to the accompaniment of nuclear "binding losses" in the form of radiation from within the sun. Not only does this steady creation of radiant energy largely explain the sun's enduring power, but the fact that the ever-growing mass of helium is light enough to rise to the relatively cool photospheric surface makes clear how the radiation is restrained and controlled, for the inert helium, a "rare gas" on earth, is not chemically susceptible and does not absorb radiation but confines it like a blanket that thickens every year. In this way it increases the sun's internal pressure and heat and magnetic energy, and starts new kinds of nuclear transformations that produce still more energy — thus prolonging for indefinite billions of years the vitality and brightness of our paternal star.

The fact that the sun is only an ordinary star, though larger than most if you count all the dwarfs, makes this scrutiny of his make-up the more important, for what goes on in the sun must be a fair sample of the kind of activity to be expected all over the heavens. Indeed, far-fetched though it seems at first glance, if we understand the sun we understand the average star.

Another, even more fundamental, step in this understanding was taken when Sir Arthur Eddington, the great astrophysicist, discovered a definite relationship between mass and luminosity — in other words, a simple rule for the tonnage of a star that must be behind every ton of starshine. He saw that the sun's light could not be attributed to size alone, for there are dark clouds in space much bigger than the sun which show no glim or glow in them at all. But a concentrated mass, he reasoned, is different. Mass (felt on Earth as weight) creates pressure which produces heat which makes light. His chain of logic put into mathematical form showed why the sun, a million times more massive than the earth, must be dazzlingly luminous; why other bodies with only a tenth of the sun's mass can glow but faintly; and any with less than a hundredth must be too dark to be visible except to their closest neighbors and would not therefore be considered real stars.

But if the lower limit of a star is a mass too slight to produce the internal pressure needed for glowing, there is an upper limit also where the star mass is so tremendous its internal pressure exceeds that produced by gravity and it must explode. Eddington deduced the upper limit as a natural consequence of the accepted rule that radiation pressure increases as the fourth power of the temperature. According to this seemingly drastic law of nature, when any mass has increased enough to double its internal temperature, its radiation pressure must have risen sixteen (double to the fourth power) times, which explains why stars are not infrequently seen exploding, and none has been found with a mass as much as a thousand times the sun's. The obvious limits thus placed both on the amount of stellar gas needed to create starlight and the quantity that will stay in one piece makes the mass of any star definitely critical and well accounts for the sun's similarity in mass to most of his companions.

A good illustration of how the balancing of pressures actually works inside a star is astronomer Fred Hoyle's calculation that if the sun were made of metal and rock like the earth, his internal heat and pressure, being vastly greater than the earth's, would vaporize and condense this molten material so fast that the collapse of the sun "would be visible to the naked eye." Yet even then the sun would not shrink indefinitely, for the shrinkage would naturally raise his temperature and pressure still higher and, when he had shrunk to about half his present size, "the internal pressure would become sufficient to support the overlying layers" and the collapse would stop.

The extremely high temperature thus needed inside a star to balance its pressures naturally ensures that its surface will be relatively cooler, for the same reason that the earth's surface is cooler than its compressed interior, and this has a damping effect on the star's energy flow or radiation outward, incidentally budgeting its strength and greatly prolonging its life. Were the sun's surface not thus kept cool but permitted to get as hot as his center, he would be "a million million times as bright" as he is and would vaporize the earth in a few minutes, although he would have to pay for this prodigal splurge by burning himself out in a relatively early end.

It is true that the synthesis of helium inside the sun adds to his supply of energy and enables him to maintain his size, but the sun or any star would go on radiating light for a long time, even if he were made of nothing but water vapor or cheese or old brick ends. For his radiation comes from his mass and is only budgetatively affected by the chemistry of his material. Indeed, according to Hoyle, if he were made of rubble, the sun would not only go on shining, he would shine at "about 1,000 times" his present rate, because "a sun composed of rock rather than largely of hydrogen would require a substantially higher internal temperature to maintain the pressure balance."

You may have been wondering, in connection with all this, how in the world our amazing sun ever got lit up in the first place. Where do suns come from anyhow? And, incidentally, how did the planets get involved — including the earth and moon?

These questions all naturally go together, for there is hardly any doubt left that the whole solar system was created simultaneously and that something similar happens in the case of other stars. The best modern theory seems to be that all stars originate from elemental gas, and that the sun, like his far-flung brothers, was born of a cloud of hydrogen and a few other gases probably mixed with dust. Under the same cloud was the earth conceived and formed along with Jupiter and all the rest of the solar congregation, even, no doubt, some members that are now missing. This primordial building material of the universe is still barely detectable throughout space in the form of extremely thin haze or gas that nevertheless amounts in its total to about 2 percent of the mass of all the stars and planets of the Milky Way, and it apparently continues to coagulate into clouds here and there.

The most acceptable theory as to what makes the elemental atoms of gas and later the molecules and microscopic dust grains (averaging less than 1/100,000 of an inch in diameter) collect into these dense birth clouds is that the pressure of light does it — for, especially in the case of fine space dust, light acts something like gravity, causing every two neighboring particles to attract each other on the average by "a force varying inversely as the square of the distance between them." Light does this by pushing its way outward from all stars in all directions with a strength that, although too small for ordinary observation, is plainly manifest in comets' tails, as we have seen. But the one direction from which light cannot push a dust mote is the direction of another mote whose shadow falls upon it, a fact which inevitably reduces average light pressure between particles, in effect drawing them together.

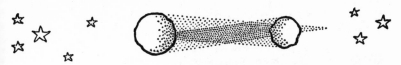

Of course this method of cloud production is slow, being (as surely as anything can be) the work of one of the great elemental "mills of God" so famous for "grinding slowly." Yet calculation shows that each passage of a million years brings noticeable changes, and a hundred million years makes literally worlds of difference. For one thing, there is a natural acceleration in the process because the nearer each particle gets to its neighbors the greater must be the relative shade upon it; and the denser the whole cloud has come to be, the less chance the subdued light inside it has of resisting the inward pressure of the full starlight outside; while every increase in density and mass inevitably builds up gravity toward a noticeable quantity.

Eventually, of course, there must arrive a point where the gravity is as strong as the light pressure. In the case of a dust cloud with the same mass of material as the sun, this works out to be when the diameter of the cloud has shrunk to some 6,000,-000,000,000 miles, or about 60,000 times the distance from Earth to sun. Quite an extensive cloud, you'll agree, yet from then on it will be settling together faster, ever faster, until in a few hundred million years from its beginning it has formed tremendous lumps into which so many particles have fallen that their size and mass and pressure and heat have built up so high that they begin to glow — and they are stars!

Don't get the idea that this apparently simple sequence of starbirth and sunbirth is without its complexities, however, nor its ramifications free of controversy. For although it has recently become a widely accepted theory among astronomers, there is plenty of room for argument, especially about its details. As no

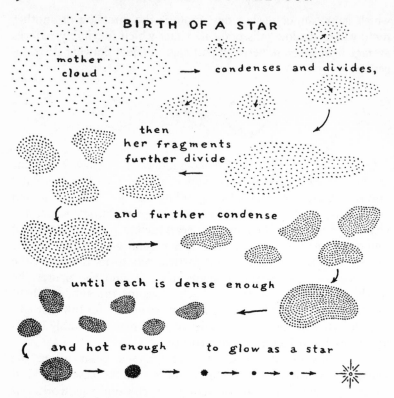

BIRTH OF A STAR

mother cloud → condenses and divides,

then her fragments further divide ←

and further condense →

until each is dense enough ←

and hot enough   to glow as a star

one can yet be very positive about what churns the Milky Way, so it is out of the question, with our present knowledge, to be dogmatic about the stirrings of the cosmic dust that spawned it, even though similar creative gyrations are right now apparently going on in plain sight of us in space clouds all over the sky where baby stars are being rocked in their inscrutable cradles of immensity. Fact is, star motion is tantalizingly slow. Yet great things are surely taking place among the stars, and the momentum of our galaxy must have been imparted in some degree to the primordial cloud which was to become the household of the sun, and the laws of thermodynamics, of magneto-hydrodynamics and of turbulence must have created eddies in it around the central mass which could form knots or nodes that might ultimately turn into the focal cores of planets and moons.

At least that is the gist of the most convincing hypothesis of the birth of the solar system, ironically published by Weizsäcker in Germany in the critical war year of 1943, when death rained from the earthly sky upon every side yet could not destroy the smallest detail of his celestial concept. It is a beautiful abstraction, this theory, and rings true for the musician and the poet as well as the chemist and the mathematician, and the steady accumulation of astronomical facts ever since has generally supported it.

Weizsäcker started with Immanuel Kant's famous eighteenth-century thesis that the original, nebulous rotating sun ejected rings of gas from its equator by centrifugal force and that these rings, which looked something like Saturn's, only much bigger and fatter, eventually broke up into separate puffs and condensed by gravitation into planets. The idea was further developed and popularized in 1796 by Pierre Simon de Laplace, the French mathematician, but sixty years later was disproved by James Clerk Maxwell, the English physicist, who showed conclusively that gravity would have been far too feeble to lump any sun rings into planets, just as it is now too feeble to produce the slightest detectable clot in the paper-thin rings of Saturn.

Although this rejection of the Kant-Laplace presumption led to a return to favor of the older theory (originated by Georges de Buffon) that the sun must have had a near collision with some other large body, with the planets evolving from the splash of tidal impact, Weizsäcker was able to clear up virtually all the many discrepancies in both theories by using modern chemical analysis and a much improved perspective on the matter of turbulence. By these means he demonstrated in geometric detail how worlds grow like raindrops from collisions of tiny particles in the sky, yet in elegant cellular patterns that make one think of plankton in the sea, our earth maturing only through an almost endless series of seeming "accidents" or cataclysms that try the imagination to conceive of.

Weiszsäcker's model of a prenatal solar system shows the sun clot gathering in the center while all around it the gas and planetary dust revolve, each molecule, each crumb describing its own orbit according to the classic laws of Kepler. But putting himself mentally and mathematically into the average flow of these heterogeneous seeds of worlds, Weizsäcker saw that there was a definite rhythm in the tide and laws for the traffic just as inviolable as with Saturn, though considerably more complex. While collisions kept reducing the number of individual particles, the particles that least often intersected the orbits of others naturally survived in the greatest numbers, and these least-intersecting orbits turned out to form a pattern of separate bean-shaped cells that girdled the central mass like a necklace. Although each particle's orbit, of course, had to be elliptical in relation to the dominating proto-sun, it was bean-shaped in relation to the average motion of its fellows as looked at by a hypothetical observer riding in his mind's eye around and around inside the great swirling cloud. These bean beads, furthermore, tended to be five in number (occasionally six) like the petals of common flowers because of the way their shapes fitted together, and each string of five had a similar string outside it, each necklace being about 1.7 times as big in diameter as the next inside, the whole concentric array

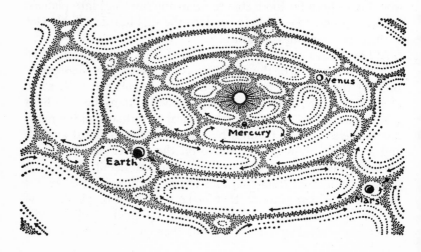

forming a simple geometric progression from the sun core all the way out to the uttermost reaches of solar influence.

In case you are wondering what all this has to do with the birth of planets, you need only look awhile at the way the mass is moving — the many bean-whirls individually rotating in the same direction while collectively they revolve in files around the sun with little counter-rotating eddies between the beans like related groups of thunder cells and geared tornadoes that have actually been observed on earth. You can see that the particles inside each rotating bean cell seldom collide because they are all going along together in the same general direction and at almost equal speeds like cars in a single wide lane of a turnpike. It is obviously the particles at the outside edges that have most of the collisions, for there they meet opposing traffic and the slightest deviation outwards is almost certain to produce a head-on crash. That would seem a bad thing on first thought to an earthly mind, but look again and you will see that these are not the crashes of death. They are actually the crashes of life! For here at the crossroads is where dust meets dust, and the beginnings of solid substances are molded that will ultimately become home and life to us all. Every collision adds its mite to some concentration of mass, and all the growing seeds or chondrules (page 117) between each two bean necklaces eventually unite into bodies the size of meteorites, then asteroids and finally into some sort of an integrated protoplanet with perhaps a few protomoons around it, and each protoplanet grows and grows, cataclysm by cataclysm, even as the face of our well-preserved moon testifies she did too, until the solar family matures into the shape we see today.

While each body evolves in this extraordinary process, it must inevitably also spin, being subjected to the continuous torque of the lesser particles pelting against it at different angles on its opposite sides — this amounting to a vast shearing action that grinds each budding world like grist in the solar mill, incidentally sorting one world from another and grading them like eggs according to their densities, in this case both internal and atmospheric densities. The cooler outer reaches of the sun's influence, for example, permit the hydrogen and other plentiful gaseous ingredients of the protoplanets to condense into liquid or solid masses heavy enough to attract by gravity more and more of similar abundant substances, which thus build the bulk of Jupiter, Saturn, Uranus and Neptune. The hotter inner regions near the sun, on the other hand, cannot hold more than a little of these more active and volatile elements, retaining instead mostly materials of high boiling point (metals and rocks) which can solidify despite the heat.

That is why the earth and its neighboring planets made of iron and nickel are so small — because the meager supply of metal was exhausted before they got big enough to compete gravitationally with the huge outer planets, which were collecting all the hydrogen within reach. And that is why there is almost no hydrogen on Earth now except in the compound forms of ice, water and water vapor. The "critical mass" (minimum body with enough gravity to hold it) for hydrogen is about the size of Uranus or Neptune. What little free hydrogen may still remain in the earth's atmosphere is believed to be still steadily escaping outward, its atomic vitality easily overcoming terrestrial gravity and enabling it to drift away to the major planets or beyond. The critical mass for helium is about Earth size, which explains the rarity of that gas on earth. And the critical mass for oxygen, nitrogen, carbon dioxide and water vapor is the size of Mars, which accounts for the borderline atmosphere there and the virtual absence of any at all on Mercury or the smaller bodies.

Thus works the natural centrifuge of our nascent star, like a cream separator or an egg-grader sorting out the stuff of the worlds, sending each element to its appointed station, each future spore of bone and brain — each fin, each foot, each feather. And the distance intervals of the planets support Weizsäcker's conclusions better than they did Bode's Law; Uranus is just twice as far from the sun as Saturn but each other planet is a little less than twice as far out as its nearest inward neighbor — the average being 1.7 times, almost exactly as in the abstract geometry of the bean necklaces. The intervals of moons likewise conform — Saturn's nine moons each average 1.8 times farther from Saturn than the next inside, and Jupiter's moons are comparable.

Of course there are vast magnetic influences (particularly among ionized gases) and many other factors and irregularities here, just as in trees and animals and clouds — which diminish not in the slightest the perfection of the whole nor fail to add immeasurably to its beauty. Can't you see Pythagoras devouring this modern orchestration of his elementary music of the spheres? Wouldn't Kepler have been fascinated?

There most likely were even more maverick moons in the early days than now, and it is possible some of those that did not escape may have just boiled away when, according to some astrophysicists, the sun briefly flared up from the sudden heat of contraction as he first settled into his present state of condensation. This may well explain why, of all known moons, our own is now the nearest to the sun, none of Venus' or Mercury's having withstood that initial "bath of fire."

Almost beyond a doubt there were also some very eccentric planets in those days, swooping about like comets, now skimming deep into the corona and close to the sun itself, now careering far out toward the other stars. One of these, it is generally allowed, may well have collided with Kepler's missing planet that could have revolved up to then between Mars and Jupiter, and whose shattered residue is as likely a source as any for the asteroids and smaller ether-corns described in the last chapter.

One could go on and on conjecturing about the sun and his family, the clues are turning up at such a rate these days. And yet most of the mystery must remain untamed behind that baleful, benevolent glare that is virtually everything we could hope for in mortal life. Only recently, Charles G. Abbot, after a lifetime of observation, came out with the conclusion that the sun is definitely one of the variable stars, pulsing regularly by as much as 2 percent. These changes, he says, are obscured by the earth's moody atmosphere but would be obvious to an astronomer on the weatherless moon — with which we up here are quick to agree. Abbot has measured as many as 64 different cycles of solar fluctuation, the longest of which is the sunspot cycle. One corresponds to a "212-day cycle noted in some studies of human pulse rates." Another matches a recognized weather period of "about six and a half days." Still others have been correlated with recurrent mental ailments, cholera, meningitis, gestation eclampsia, and even the suicide rate.

Radioastronomy has provided probably the most exciting recent data on the sun: ionic "noise storms" at radio frequencies from the almost invisible chromosphere and corona, and outbursts from sunspots that have increased "in intensity by a factor of ten million in a few minutes," while tending to repeat themselves every five days. What this may signify in solar potentiality is suggested by Hoyle's prognosis that ultimately the sun's complex nuclear processes will make him swell until he is thousands of times bigger and brighter than now, whereupon he will start his final decline until he is only a feeble ghost about a twentieth his present size, the type of star known as a white dwarf. Such drama might seem theoretical fantasy if it were not being actually observed nightly in other stars in various stages of their evolution all over the sky.

It is understandably not easy to take in the reality of even the simplest solar facts, like sunlight pushing part of the earth's ionosphere for 1,500 miles outward from the line of sunset to create a special kind of auroral glow similar to a comet's tail. I mentally gulp every time I realize that if I could drive a car at 60 m.p.h. steadily toward the sun, day and night without stopping, it would take me 175 years to get there; that if the sun's center were where the moon is, the earth would be only about halfway to his surface; or that the whole system is bearing us all at a relative speed of 12 miles a second toward a point in the sky near the star Vega, called "the apex of the sun's way." I have to stop and think to figure out why the shortest day of the year on Earth has neither the latest sunrise nor the earliest sunset, or whether that has anything to do with the sun's being three million miles nearer the earth at New Year's Day than on the Fourth of July. And what of the relationship between the sun's steady radiation loss of mass and his direct radiation feeding of plants and animals on earth?

Most wonderful of all to me is the realization that for all his terrible power, the sun is just an ordinary gentle star who rises in a loving manner, bringing life and joy to the world — that, in fact, he is perpetually rising somewhere on Earth, ever pushing his hopeful sunrise ahead of him as he trails his eternal sunset behind — that he literally twinkles to the fish in the sea as remoter stars twinkle to dwellers in the air — and that his mystic potencies have long demonstrated themselves for the common good, not just now or here but nearly always and everywhere, even unto the uttermost reaches of radiation.

7. the cousin stars

A̲S I LOOK OUT OF SPACE upon the earth and see now with my eyes what it has hardly been possible to imagine for these billions of years, the strength of distance comes to me — the power of perspective welling upward through consciousness. I think I must be really coming to a larger view. Even the old familiar stars look different now, for I can see for the first time the earth's proper place among them and feel something of how insignificant is our ancient roost in the greater company of reality.

Astronomers have pointed out that if the earth suddenly ceased to be, it probably would not be missed by anyone anywhere — except (believe me) us space pioneers — because there would be no intelligent beings left (so far as we can tell) in the solar system to notice that our moon had turned into a planet to plod on alone in the earth's footsteps. And of course, the observers on other star systems are presumed to be much too far away to have either known or much cared about such a trifling sun parasite as our tiny jot. Even the sun itself would be of interest only to those stars near by (say, within a few quadrillion miles) where there might or might not be any minds capable of studying it. Farther off, to match the increasing numbers of likely observers would be a correspondingly decreasing visibility because of distance.

Yet as we believe our own world is not just scenery, so we must appreciate that the giant stars and their galaxies are not there for mere decoration either. One can't suppress the hunch that there is some sort of tangible meaning to it all — in fact, a growing and multiple meaning — and that if one could somehow find a hundred meanings there would still be a thousand deeper ones waiting to be found.

I think the study of astronomy must be to a man somewhat as the study of a man would be to a germ dwelling inside his body, and that you and I can no more grasp the whole sky than one of our germs could conceive of us. This, of course, is aside from the debatable question of whether the organic sky in turn may better understand us than we can understand germs or ourselves. The only sure way to the stars for us, it seems, is to look at them humbly, beginning on Earth with all our human limitations — to seek perspective along with its risks to body and mind as did Thales and Pythagoras and Aristarchos and Poseidonius and Copernicus and Galileo and Kepler and Newton and many a simpler soul, an Arab herdsman or a village pariah, the kind who for ages immemorial have been laughed at for walking into wells (as Thales once did) while gazing overmuch at the heavens. Indeed, it is the few stargazers and astronomers who survived the wells and the greater hardship of ridicule, even some, perhaps, who died in the wells, who have given us much of the freedom and knowledge of the world we now live in.

So let us take heart for the tenting sky. Is it not the surest example of God's "terrible majesty . . . who laid the corner stone thereof when the morning stars sang together, and all the

sons of God shouted for joy?" Certainly the stars we can measure
live on the most lavish scale that can be sensed by the human
mind. Imagine two golf balls roaming the skies of North America,
each somewhere within a thousand miles of the ground and anywhere between Panama and the Arctic ice. Averaging thousands
of miles apart, they would seem to have plenty of elbow room,
yet they are packed just as tightly as the 200,000,000,000 stars of
the Milky Way! And Milky Ways in turn are as numerous in the
sky as grains of sand on an ocean beach!

There is no way of grasping it adequately in terms of earthly
experience, but one can try to penetrate at least the nearer depths
of sky — to begin a comprehension of the inner shell of visibility
composed of the 5,000-odd stars that are all that the sharpest
human eye can see unaided. This shell obviously is not uniform
in distance, since many of the nearest stars are too dim to see
without a telescope, while others that look near are in reality
remote but unusually bright. It is a shell composed solely of
visibility, its stars limited to the first six visual magnitudes. And
these stars, commonly referred to as "fixed," are actually in
perpetual motion — motion that seems very slow because of the
distance but often amounts to hundreds of miles per second and
is not random but part of the almost incomprehensible flow of
that river of suns we see as the Milky Way.

Beyond this first shell lies layer after layer of stars of the seventh
and fainter magnitudes, each layer composed of many more stars,
each magnitude appearing about two and a half times fainter than
the last, the fifteenth magnitude exactly one hundredth as bright
as the tenth while ten thousand times more brilliant than the
twenty-fifth, and so on. Up to the twentieth magnitude, just
beyond the limit of visibility through the 100-inch reflector on
Mount Wilson, the stars number about 500,000,000, but several
billions can be individually seen through the 200-incher at Mount
Palomar — still more caught by long-time exposures on its most
sensitive photographic plates, each star of the last layer being no
brighter than would be the beam of a pocket flashlight aimed at
us from the moon. Yet even this vast number, extending to the
twenty-fourth magnitude, is only a small fraction of the stars in

our galaxy and its outlying clusters, many of which overlap each other so densely they are literally buried in light as billions of others again are shrouded in mysterious space clouds of utter darkness.

And all the while, year in, year out, thousands of astronomers and their assistants are listing and classifying new stars in the standard catalogs. One published in nine volumes in 1924 contained data on 225,300 stars, and a recent map shows every visible star out to an average distance of 2,100,000,000,000,000 miles from Mount Palomar.

When Ptolemy compiled his great *Almagest* at the Alexandrian observatory in A.D. 140, he called the stars by name. But in modern times it has become obvious that this could not go on indefinitely, since there are more stars than all possible names of reasonable length. And anyhow, it seemed a strain on nature to have to think up longer and longer names for fainter and fainter stars, like pasting bigger and bigger labels on smaller and smaller packages until the label outweighs the package. So astronomers soon stopped thinking up titles like Almerzamonnagied or Aschimeshinermis (names of real stars) and, after they ran out of Greek letters, then Roman, reverted to Arab numerals, which, being of inexhaustible supply, are even more plentiful than the obviously finite number of all seeable and potentially seeable stars.

It is quite appropriate anyway, I think, to use Arab numerals for stars, since the Arabs, herdsmen almost to a man, sleeping in the open with their heads on their saddles, named more of the early stars than did the Greeks, and even a lot of the Greek-named stars got renamed by the Arabs during the golden age of Islam when the Abbasid editions of the *Almagest* became the foundation of cumulative scientific knowledge.

Though not quite as varied as the wind names of the world, star names to me have a fascination and beauty peculiarly their own, and are probably the most ancient and classic of all the features of the real Arabian nights. Consider Algol (*al gol*, the ghoul), who highlights the evil head of Medusa in the constellation of Perseus and was thought to have demonic powers because he pulses every third night; Thuban in the Dragon's tail, who was the North Star when the Egyptian pyramids were built; Markab and Algenib at the shoulder and rump of Pegasus; Algorab of the Raven; Arneb of the Hare; Mizar and Alioth of the Great Bear. Many have Greek names like great Arcturos or bright Sirius of the Greater Dog, Procyon of the Lesser Dog, or Castor or Canopos, or Job's dainty Pleiades, which make me think of Chopin's preludes, or the rainy Hyades, or Coma Berenices (The Hair of Berenice), a faint cluster that delicately represents lovely tresses. Some sound French or German like Fomalhaut of the Southern Fish or Japanese like Nunki of Sagittarius the Archer. One is suggestive of an Oriental sneeze: Rho Ophiuchi! But most of them are obviously Arabic: Suhail, Alatrab, Zarijan, Nijad, Salib, Mebsuta, Mibwala, Zaban, Unuk, Ghurab, Ruchbar, Sabik, Sagma, Ajmal, Theemim, Phegda, Huzmat . . . I could go on and on indefinitely. It is like reading Sinbad the Sailor's almanac, this roll-call of the orbs. Can you feel the rhythm in it? Merach, Almach, Megrez, Furud, Urkab, Iclil, Jahfalah, Zavijava, Zubenesch, Mabsutah, Difda, Murzim, Chenib . . . drifting at random across the scarcely charted ocean of silent suns. It seems a pity that they ever switched to initials — Alpha Librae, Beta Capricorni, Gamma Virginis, Iota this, Mu that — or mere numerrals: Catalog No. L886–6 or C.D.–36 ° 15693. But the actual heavens have turned out to be so far beyond human comprehension that nothing less abstract than pure mathematics could seriously hope to keep up with them. On earth it would be like stripping Chicago down to 42 ° N. 88 ° W., its bare address its full title — the irreducible essence of identification.

The stars themselves, however, naturally hold far more of wonder than their names. Although they are fundamentally much alike, being balls of glowing gas about 80 percent hydrogen and 15 percent helium and nine tenths of them between one tenth and ten times as massive as the sun, their variety in appearance, volume and density is startling. There is a remote star

called S Doradus in the larger of the Magellanic Clouds that is 400,000,000,000 times as bright as the dimmest star known — and if you could line up the two an equal distance away (even in a diffusionless vacuum), you would not see the dim one at all because of the extreme contrast in luminosity. The volume of another and virtually nameless star quite near us, an invisible infra-red member of a family unit called Epsilon Aurigae, is great enough to contain most of our solar system, including the 5½-billion-mile circumference of Saturn's orbit, and is about 100,000,-000,000,000,000 times as big as the smallest star known, which has a diameter of only 2,500 miles and is literally smaller than some moons. Such giants as this E Aurigae component — now known as E Aurigae I (for Infra-red) — are sometimes described as "red-hot vacuums" because their material, though hot, averages thousands of times thinner than earthly air and is normally invisible, so that you might fly through them for days in your insulated space ship without even realizing you were inside a star. At the other extreme are white dwarfs with a density 60,000,000,000,000 times greater, where any mountains would instantly flatten from their own weight of 600 tons per cubic inch, where it would take a powerful jack to raise a grain of sand and the faintest wisp of cigarette smoke would clunk to the ground like a shovelful of bird shot.

A large percentage of the stars are definitely irregular in one way or another. Like people, stars are apt to express themselves in their social relationships. Nearly half do not dwell alone as does our bachelor sun but have somehow picked up a mate to dance with around and around a common center of gravity. At least 2 percent are believed to be triplet or quadruplet suns. Some turn out to be quintuplets like Epsilon Lyrae or sextuplets like Castor or Mizar, or a cluster of some larger number that circle in very complex orbits around each other. Many have thick turbulent atmospheres of their own besides those of their probable planets and in some cases even of their moons. Some throb rhythmically as if from an internal sequence of atomic interchange. Some tick almost like clocks, some flash a kind of code in dots and dashes, some seem to breathe, some just change their color and brightness slowly and irregularly, some seem to smolder, some fume or smoke or spit, some actually explode.

How rich we are that we can look on these worlds with the perspective of modern science, with precise knowledge garnered and established by thousands of trained astronomers over hundreds of years with the help of billions of dollars' worth of equipment — that we do not have to wonder as did former men whether stars are jewels dangling from celestial drapery or peepholes in the astral skin of creation!

The explanations for stars and their behavior go back over the horizon of antiquity in many forms, but that the profundity of these perennial asphodels of light was recognized from earliest times is established beyond doubt by cuneiform inscriptions and hieroglyphics in which the sign for God was always a star. It is written that a strange star over Bethlehem literally introduced the new-born Christ to the people of the earth. Sabianism or star-worship is the oldest known religion and is, of course, tied in with the fact that certain stars were guides to herdsmen and farmers in their seasonal activities and to sailors and explorers navigating the trackless seas and deserts of the world.

We still allow that "Sirius rising with the sun (about July 23) marks the dog days well begun," because this Dog Star, worshiped by the Egyptians as the "Bringer of the Nile" and known to Job as Mazzaroth, was once thought to produce the heat (and high water) of summer by adding his fire to the sun god's. Ancient sailors used to swear by the zodiacal sign of Gemini, the twin stars (Castor and Pollux), and so do we — by Jiminy! The curious and powerful concept of the zodiac (the sequence of constellations in the sun's annual path) seems to have originated in Asia Minor or Armenia. Certainly it represents the kinds of animals and views of the heavens then seen in that region. But the Chinese had a modest four-sign zodiac of their own, comprised of *Tsing Lung*, the azure dragon; *Heung Woo*, the dark warrior; *Choo Neaou*, the red bird; and *Pih Hoo*, the white tiger.

The HARE   PERSEUS   The SWAN   The TWINS

Everywhere the animistic pantheism naturally created constellation symbols, and gradually established the eighty-eight constellation titles that serve modern astronomy today. These range through all sorts of odd things that were once thought to have magic powers: *Musca*, the fly; *Norma*, the carpenter's square; *Indus*, the Indian; *Reticulum*, the net; *Pyxis*, the box or compass . . . They include household furniture, from *Mensa*, the table, to *Fornax*, the kitchen stove; several parts of a ship like *Vela*, the sail; *Carina*, the keel, and *Puppis*, the poop; eight occupations (not counting *Virgo's*) from painter to snake charmer; a dozen tools and inventions, including some surprisingly modern ones like *Antlia*, the air pump; *Telescopium*, the telescope; *Microscopium*, the microscope; *Sextans*, the sextant; *Octans*, the octant; and thirteen species of living mammals, eight of birds, and a full dozen assorted reptiles, arthropods and fish. Hardly to mention also the mythical creatures and the many legends that have accumulated about these seemingly endless celestial hosts.

Our Big Dipper, for instance, seems to have once been that

Greek nymph named Callisto. She was an outdoor girl and had talent in the song and dance and also, it is said, used to go hunting — for what sort of game one asks not. But it appears unlikely to have been four-legged game, because Greek legend indicates she aroused so much jealousy in Queen Hera, matron of the gods, that Hera, having determined to cool her off, turned her into a polar bear and banished her to the Arctic skies. And to keep her from getting too earthy again, Hera also stipulated that the Bear constellation could never retire below the horizon as most other stars do. And that, they say, is why the Big Dipper trudges round and round the pole, never escaping Hera's watchful eye — at least not as viewed from anywhere north of the latitude of Greece. So poor Callisto knows now only too well what can come from getting in another woman's hair. Indeed, the locks of Berenice were placed right under her nose, just to remind her. And she must have many a wistful memory as she circles eternally around the pole, accompanied also by the small but sobering memento: her baby son Arcas, the cub bear or Little Dipper whose tail in our time contains the North Star.

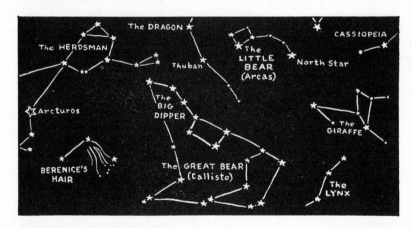

Speaking of the North Star, which is more specifically called Polaris, I think it is worth some scrutiny as a sample of what the sky holds in store everywhere. Of course, Polaris is a fairly ordinary star except for the chance fact that at present the earth's axis is aimed within one degree of it, yet it has its secret life to unfold to modern astronomers. Even in a small telescope it becomes two stars, one of which in larger magnification turns out to be a "brilliant supergiant" that has been spectroscopically analyzed as "double" in turn, having a close but invisible companion. The supergiant itself has also recently been found to be variable, pulsing with a heartbeat of four days, and its unseen mate (according to the spectroscope) circles around it once every 30 years at a range of a few hundred million miles, while the visible and much remoter cousin takes several millenniums, even though it is only 18½ seconds of arc away by visual angle. And as if this were not amazing enough, the largest telescopes have spotted two more members of Polaris' family at the delicate angles of 43″ and 82″, thus relegated to such slow orbits that it has not yet been possible to prove that they will ever complete a circuit around the central giant. Most significant of all to me, however, and requiring an almost celestial effort of mind to comprehend, is the fact that these five stars (or are there still more?), along with their possible unseen planets, moons, asteroids, comets and meteorites, occupying many thousands of times as much space as our solar system, are all contained in the gentle twinkle of Polaris, the tip of Arcas' innocent tail, that has been showing the north to unsuspecting seafaring men for some thousands of years

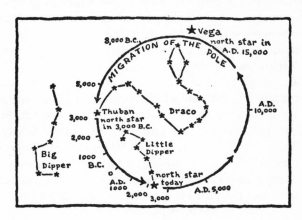

and still today guides everything from submarines to flying freighters to intercontinental missiles on their journeyings of peace or war about the earth. The fact that Polaris is only temporarily the North Star is, of course, attributable to the earth's precessing like a wobbling top, its axis describing a slow circuit about a bigger axis every twenty-six thousand years or so, within which time Vega takes its turn at being the North Star and the Southern Cross hovers over New York betwixt less orderly and perhaps less misleading eons that I like to think Job envisioned when he declared God "stretcheth out the north over the empty place, and hangeth the earth upon nothing."

♈   ♉   ♊   ♋   ♌   ♍

Algol, the pulsing demon of Arabia, is another star with a story which not only awed the ancients but posed one of the greatest riddles modern astronomers have ever solved. As the most famous of the variables, its message of dots and dashes was early decoded to mean that Algol is really a binary, consisting of twin stars revolving around each other in the remarkably short period of 2 days, 20 hours, 48 minutes and 53.8 seconds, the dash being accurately interpreted as a deep eclipse of the brighter star as the dimmer one passed in front of it, the dot a slight reduction in light as the dimmer one in turn was hidden. But although spectroscopic and other analyses of the light gave a lot more information, the astronomers were still uncertain as to how total were the eclipses and therefore as to what were the actual sizes, luminosities and relative brightnesses of the two stars.

Since the toughest scientific nuts are often cracked by variously assuming some key fact on which to build full-scale hypotheses for testing until some hypothesis proves true, the astronomers assumed at first that the two stars had the normal binary mass ratio of two to one. That was in 1911, and it made the bigger twin half as massive as our sun which, according to well-established mass-luminosity graphs, indicated it should be much dimmer than it obviously was. Thus the big question: which should be believed, the mass-ratio table or the mass-luminosity graph?

The nutcracker was wielded by two astronomers named Richard A. Rossiter and Dean B. McLaughlin at Ann Arbor Observatory, who had the rare imagination to figure out a way to get the missing masses by calculating the diameter of Algol's brighter twin, even though the most powerful telescopes showed the whole of Algol only as a single pinpoint of light. Their key step was to clock the star's roll through the sky, to measure the rotational velocity of its equator in miles per second by a method used previously only on the sun. They reasoned that if they could somehow observe first one edge of it, then the opposite "limb," measuring how fast one side was coming toward them and the other going away, by its doppler (wave frequency) effect on the spectrum, they could get an accurate result. But the sun, whose disk can easily be blocked off to reveal any segment separately, is a very different matter than a distant star. How could they possibly cover up part of a mere point of light?

The Algol System

SIMPLE AND COMPLEX MULTIPLE-STAR SYSTEMS

The answer was: *they* couldn't. Yet Algol could. That is where the imagination came in. Rossiter and McLaughlin correctly visualized that the eclipsing stars would cover each other's edges one after the other as they crossed over, just as the moon makes a crescent out of the sun immediately before and after a total solar eclipse. Even though Algol was much too far away for them to hope ever to see the crescents, they could calculate the exact moments when Algol's light must come from the crescents and thus accurately record it, limb by limb, in the spectroscope. In this remarkable way they finally succeeded in finding the star's speed of rotation. As they had already surmised its period of rotation (day), which must match its interval of revolution (year) in such a close stellar partnership, it was a

simple matter to calculate its diameter (2,550,000 miles), which
is now probably better established than the dimensions of any
other star except the sun.

With that elusive key in hand at last, the mass ratio between
the two stars was easily determined as five to one. And a short
while later, the reason for the original wrong assumption in this
ratio appeared with the discovery of a slight biennial weaving
motion in Algol's course through the sky, which led to the detection of a third member of the family, one that is so much heavier
than the other two that they both revolve around it in a period
of just under two years. It now became clear that the light
coming from Algol during its dash intervals, when the bright
twin is covered by the dim one, is not the light of the dim twin
alone (being much too bright for that) but mostly the light of the
sly aunt or third member, who is aloof enough (20,000,000 miles
away) to shine continuously without interference.

You might not think that such painstaking detective work in
unraveling the mysterious twinkle of an inconspicuous star would
influence life on Earth much, yet the lives not only of men but
nations have hung and will again hang on lesser things. Think
of the case of Orion, the mighty Nimrod of our winter sky, and his
string of hunting dogs, who may have influenced the outcome of
World War II. I am not referring here so much to Procyon, "the
water spaniel at the stream" (Milky Way), as to the big dog
Sirius and his little white-dwarf companion (known since 1844
but first seen by accident when an optician in 1862 was testing a
new big object-glass), now designated by the subtitle B. If you
feel like smiling when you contemplate this dog-star puppy, you'd
better be serious because, made of stuff that weighs eighteen tons
a pint, it is not to be taken lightly, and even its name sounds like
a schoolmaster admonishing a giggly pupil, "B Sirius!" or, more
customarily, Sirius B. Stranger still, the mighty mite (almost as
heavy as the sun but shedding only ⅟₃₆₀ as much light) was not

only the first invisible star to be generally recognized (by the big dog's limping gait) but was the one star in all the heavens, as we shall understand later (page 585), which could help Einstein most in proving his general relativity theory. The acceptance of Einstein, of course, led, among other things, to major efforts in atomic research and to the A-bombs that so decisively raised the siege of Japan.

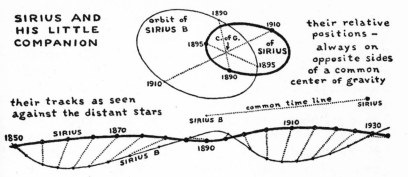

SIRIUS AND HIS LITTLE COMPANION

their relative positions — always on opposite sides of a common center of gravity

their tracks as seen against the distant stars

If modern research has already loosed "the bands of Orion," perhaps it will some day also "bind the sweet influences" of the Pleiades. In the meantime, it is appropriate at least to consider this delicate confluence of stars, since the very word "consider" derives from "con" and "sider," meaning a gathering of stars. Astronomers have worshiped and admired these graceful daughters of Atlas ever since, as the legend goes, they were pursued and frightened by Orion and ran away through the starry meadows to hide in the soft mane of Taurus the bull, where they still are and where, in the telescope, you can actually see the veily nebulosity around them. The Pleiades were mentioned in Chinese literature in 2357 B.C., when Alcyone, brightest of them, was very near the "point" occupied by the sun at vernal equinox. The Romans named them Atauria, "the darlings of the bull." Other peoples at various times have called them "the rosette of diamonds," "the hen and chickens," "the swarm of fireflies," "the shining drops of dew," "the seven virgins." Their date of setting was the ancient signal for the spring sowing of grain.

In South Africa they became "rimestars" because their coming
heralded the autumn frosts. The Great Pyramid is closely associated with them, and Greek temples were oriented to their position
as early as 1530 B.C., later including the Parthenon.

Traditionally used as a test of vision, the Pleiades appear as five
stars to some persons, while most others see six, and a few with
the sharpest eyes (or imaginations) seven or more, the seventh
presumably being purple Pleione, a strange potent star recently
discovered to be spinning so fast it has flattened into a kind of
flying saucer with a dark red ring of hydrogen continuously
flowing out from its violet core, a fact which is doubtless a key
factor in its borderline visibility. Modern binoculars, however,
bring the Pleiades out by the dozen, and a small telescope can
sprout nearly a hundred. Contrary to most constellations which
only *appear* to be together, like an airplane brushing the moon, the
Pleiades are an open cluster of young stars moving as a real unit
through space, their mysterious and beautiful mane clouds along
with them, perhaps dominating the life or weather on some of
their planets and moons. Their queen Alcyone, blazing with the
light of three thousand suns, in fact would be the tyrant of our
nights were she as near as Alpha Centauri or Sirius but, being
twelve million diameters of the earth's orbit away, her regal glance
is tempered by its 325 years of travel to our sight. Which, of
course, is part of her power of fascination, for it is admittedly,
a strain for a human mind to grasp that the same light we see to-
night from these celestial sisters, including shy Merope, sweet
Taygeta, Sterope and little Pleione, had already been moving
toward us for a century and a half when George Washington
was elected the first president of thirteen newly united states.

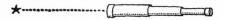

Less of a consideration than the Pleiades but of its own special
interest is the nearest star to our sun, collectively known as Alpha

Centauri (of the constellation Centaurus), which, as you may have suspected, likewise turns out to be multiple and its main member (Alpha Centauri A) the closest replica of the sun so far discovered anywhere. Although the fact that the center of this system is composed of two medium stars was noticed by telescope way back in 1689, it was not until 1915 that a faint eleventh-magnitude star was discovered two full degrees away circling slowly around them both and obviously part of the same family. And this little reddish dwarf that is only the size of a medium planet but a thousand times heavier is the closest known individual star to the sun (in distance) in the whole heavens, a mere 25,000,000,000,000 miles away! Now famous on earth as Proxima Centauri, it is an insignificant little thing that would not have been noticed but for its nearness, and it may well go unnoticed still by any stargazers of Alpha Centauri A or B since it apparently describes an elongated orbit that averages something like 800,000,000,000 miles from its two big brothers and takes many thousands of years for each circuit. Even though it periodically flares up to double its brightness, it averages less than 1/10,000 of our sun's brilliance, and is barely a speck in our biggest telescopes.

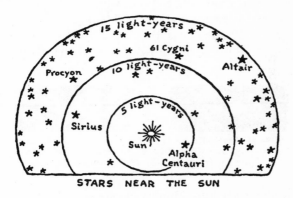

STARS NEAR THE SUN

That there must be many such dwarfs roaming the skies seems evident from the fact that at least five (or 25 percent) of the twenty nearest-known stars are definitely dwarfs and several others are stunted in various degrees. Stars still unknown, of course, are apt to be dwarfish also, like the shy red pigmy twins discovered in 1948 by Dr. Willem J. Luyten only six light-years away, which makes them at present the nearest-known stars to the sun except for the Alpha Centauri family, even as they drift off at a languid 26 miles a second. Both these stars, incidentally, are enveloped in huge cloudy atmospheres of incandescent hydrogen and calcium gas. And the fainter of the two, only $\frac{1}{60,000}$ as bright as the sun, demonstrated a startling flare-up on December 7, 1948, increasing to twelve times its normal brightness, then subsiding, all in twenty minutes — a unique and unexplained "atomic explosion" estimated by Dr. Luyten as equivalent to "a billion atomic bombs." Luyten, by the way, is the world's leading small-star fancier, having discovered some 5,000 dwarfs, including nearly 400 white ones among which is the smallest star known: about 25 light-years from Earth and only half again as big as our moon though weighing 40 percent more than the sun.

Any of these dwarfs may just possibly be ready to explode, because they are of such dense material that their atoms quite likely had to collapse in their shrinking process, perhaps even combining electrons and protons into neutrons under the terrific pressure and leaving them in an unstable state. Certainly today's astronomers will remember the dwarf WZ Sagittae, which exploded in 1913 and again in 1946, on each occasion brightening about a thousand times, then fading away to a tiny white spark — and such flare stars as the nearby red dwarf Kruger 60 B, which periodically

Two photographs of the star system Kruger 60 showing smaller star B normal (left) and flaring (right) only 135 seconds later

lights up with such astonishing suddenness. There has been a growing consensus on the nuclear temperament of dwarfs, many astronomers concluding that the majority of them are just senile stars made of "degenerate gas" living economically like old people on pensions who presently will die, their corpses thereafter slowly turning from white to red and finally into "black dwarfs" to cruise endlessly and invisibly on and on through space as count-less millions may already be doing.

Some "dead" dwarfs might even become planets, according to the definition of a planet as a nonglowing body on an orbit around a star, but obviously their great density would make them vastly different from anything in the solar system, and any animal life that grew upon them would need something less gravity-sensitive than legs to move around on. However, the common run of multiple stars in the sky may also develop much greater planets than ours, as is suggested by the dark body "fifteen times as mas-sive as Jupiter" recently spotted hovering around the near-by bi-nary, 61 Cygni. And there may be many such borderline planets, almost massive enough to glow, in the bigger star houses — to say nothing of planets with irregular and eccentric orbits moving around complex multi-suns which light them up on both sides at once so they know no night, have never seen twilight and probably know nothing of stars except their own local suns. Some double stars are thought to be so close together that their atmos-pheres actually overlap, permitting small intense stars to revolve inside the outer limits of large diffuse stars. Beta Lyrae is an overlapping binary in which the smaller star receives a steady stream of incandescent hydrogen gas from the larger one, letting

THE SPOUTING BINARY OF BETA LYRAE

it overflow in turn through an endless red wake into space. Others, such as Capella, the classical Goat of Auriga, may turn out to be two that touch each other only once in their revolutions — in

Capella's case, of 104 days' duration — forming a brief intermittent "double sun" of incandescent gas shaped like a dumbbell. Besides the instability of such a condition, with its friction of clashing gases which obviously cannot go on touching and separating with unchanged rhythm indefinitely, such a system would seem pretty unfavorable to life. Certainly any planets circling the embracing stars would be bound to pass through zones of widely differing gases and temperatures, their creatures perhaps subsisting on oxygen on their version of Tuesdays, but having to breath methane on Thursdays and a blend of ammonia and formaldehyde on Friday nights, to say nothing of putting up with a terrific ordeal by fire every summer — a flame bath that would drive the very rocks to ruth as the neighbor sun swept its closest and all the moons flared up like hot coals, sprouting bright comet tails across the sky.

Other seemingly inhospitable stars are the radioactive ones that put out hard x-rays or deadly gamma-rays, either of which would soon tear apart any planetary molecules that had approached the complexity which appears essential for what we call life. And there are the hot, shrunken Wolf-Rayet stars that eject gas streams at velocities up to 2,000 miles a second, and the cool "carbon stars" that, when their surfaces fall to 3500° F., "must shower out a rain of soot." And of course, a whole assortment of pulsating ones that throb, not from eclipsing partners like Algol, but from some mysterious internal chemical rhythm, only dimly understood,

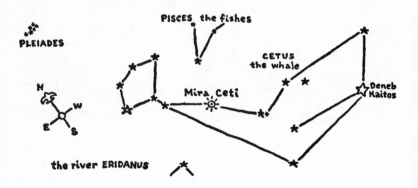

which amounts, in the case of red-giant stars, to a continual series of lesser or greater explosions that are usually irregular both in timing and intensity. The best-known of these is famous Mira Ceti, the huge "miracle star" appropriately situated in the constellation of the Whale, which, like Moby Dick, is wont to disappear altogether for months at a time and was considered sacred by Fabricius, the Frisian pastor who discovered it in 1596.

A slightly different kind of variable that explodes in predictable proportion to its rhythm is exemplified by U Geminorum, a star that may flare up a hundredfold in brightness every 97 days. It is obviously related to the star AB Draconis known to puff up to fifteen times normal every fortnight and to a broad class of other U Geminorum explosive types that follow the same rule of keeping a strict proportion between change in magnitude and interval, all multiplying their brilliance at each flare-up by about 3 percent more than the number of days from one outburst to the next. Thus: 100 times brighter each 97 days; 60 times each 58; 15 times each 14, and so forth.

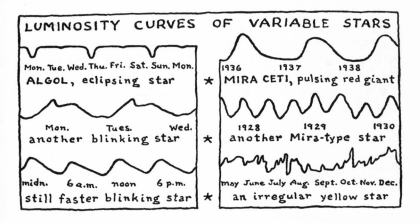

Still another kind of variable is the Cepheid, named after its best-known representative in the constellation Cepheus, whose periods are short and very regular and with an amazing uniformity of relationship between interval and absolute (not relative or apparent) brightness. The central supergiant star of Polaris, for example, is a Cepheid of four-day period. Some astronomers think that Cepheids are really huge single stars in the act of breaking into two, their regular fluctuations of magnitude caused by the fact that their elongated birth-shapes reveal alternately brighter and dimmer surfaces as they spin. Others theorize that they are spherical "geysers of fire" expanding and shrinking every few days. But their surest trait is that those whose interval is one day long turn out to be all of the same actual brightness and those with a ten-day period about four times as bright, with others ranged proportionately between. It is almost as if these strange worlds were ancient beacons on a mountain with people on it gathering fuel so steadfastly between fires that the longer they work collecting brushwood the brighter the succeeding blaze in exact proportion. And the wonderful thing about the Cepheid's fixed relationship between time and absolute brightness is that it provides astronomers with an accurate way of measuring distances to remote stars even millions of light-years off in space. Before 1912 there was no known means of getting the range of any but the closest stars, those few so near that by surveying them very precisely at six-month intervals (time for the earth to move to the opposite side of the sun), their distance could be calculated by parallax or geometric triangulation. But now if an astronomer can just spot a Cepheid and take its pulse, he knows immediately how much light it should radiate and therefore, by the brightness or dimness of its appearance (using a simple equation), how far away it should be. And the fact that Cepheids happen to be dazzlingly yellow supergiant stars widely distributed throughout the sky and so bright they can be picked out individually even in foreign galaxies has led to their wide acceptance as the "milestones of the universe."

A still more spectacular kind of variable is the temporary or surprise star, which suddenly lights up where there was apparently nothing before and blazes brightly for a few weeks only to fade back out of sight all in the same year. The first such star ever recorded burst into visibility in the constellation of Scorpio in 134 B.C., and, according to Pliny the historian, was spotted by Hipparchos of Nicaea, the greatest astronomer of antiquity, who called it the "nova" because it was "new" and different from all others previously seen, in fact, as he said, "one born in my own age!"

Up to then, the world had regarded the fixed stars as absolutely sacred and changeless, but this mysterious object dramatically demonstrated that stars on the contrary may come and go, and it served to stimulate Hipparchos into creating the world's first exact and comprehensive sky catalog, which listed the number, brightness and position of every star he could see "in order that even the least of these should not pass unnoticed" — a task which impressed Pliny as "a presumptuous scheme even for a god" but which started the earliest program of systematic celestial observation on Earth, and for which modern astronomers will never cease to be grateful.

As the centuries passed, other novae appeared from time to time — the star of Bethlehem could well have been one — and at present, by international synoptic collaboration and electronic comparison of regularly photographed sky sections, they are turning up at an average rate of one every ten days. Even though many fewer than one percent become bright enough to be visible to the naked eye, spectrography reveals nova light to come from gases first bursting outward, then collapsing inward at speeds of thousands of miles a second, the confused spectral lines shifting toward violet, then red, in striking contrast to the sharp steady lines of the calm normal star. The atoms are obviously subjected to such violence that they lose electrons and exhibit the characteristic spectral signature of ionization with shifting lines that has come to mean "nova." This, of course, is strong evidence of the explosive atomic nature of the phenomenon, and is often corroborated, when the nova is not too far away, by actual sight of the dissipating gases, or even (as in the case of Nova Hercules in 1934) of separating pieces of the star itself during the years following the outburst. The outburst, moreover, having come to be associated with white dwarfs, is now believed to signalize not the blooming of new stars but more likely (as hinted on page 176) the death agony and collapse of old ones.

Even if you don't consider a flare-up of a hundredfold in brightness an explosion, there is a type of nova called the supernova, which suddenly increases a billion times in brightness and whose gases have been measured to shoot out at more than a hundred thousand miles a second. That is an explosion by anybody's definition and, incidentally, it is the biggest kind of explosion ever seen by the naked eye anywhere. The only bigger ones are the almost unimaginable explosions of whole galaxies or of the universe itself, as we will see in the next chapter. No supernova in our Milky Way galaxy, however, can yet have been studied with modern methods, because none has occurred since 1604, five years before Galileo's telescope. But a number of remote ones have been seen and photographed in other galaxies, like the supernova of 1885 in our neighboring Andromeda galaxy (1,500,000 light-years away) and one whose light reached us in March 1950 from a galaxy seven times farther off, where it must have originally exploded some 10,000,000 years before the animals of earth had ever dreamed they could evolve such creatures as men. There is even some evidence of a double supernova having occurred within the last few millenniums in the large Magellanic Cloud.

The first humanly documented supernova seems to have been the one described in conservative Chinese annals as the "guest star" of A.D. 1054, which appeared "several fingers southeast of T'ien-kuan [Zeta Tauri]" and was probably the most stupendous observed outburst in all history. The spectacle amazed humanity and was recorded in pictures on both sides of the earth, even in Indian rock drawings in northern Arizona, where it was depicted rising beside the crescent moon in what was later calculated to be exactly the right circumstances for an hour before dawn on the morning of July 5, 1054, perfectly matching the Japanese and

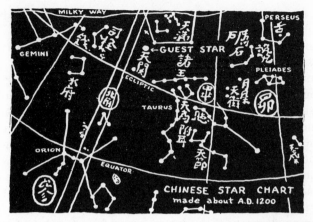

CHINESE STAR CHART
made about A.D. 1200

Chinese records. Like the almost similar supernova observed by Tycho Brahe in November 1572, this one for a time outshone all other stars in the sky, its iridescent yellow glare plain to see in broad daylight. It could well have been the brightest celestial object, other than the sun, ever to be beheld by historic man. Even though it occurred twelve years before William the Conqueror landed in England and faded from prominence within a few weeks, lingering in faint visibility for less than two years, the mark

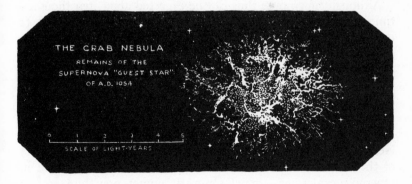

THE CRAB NEBULA
REMAINS OF THE
SUPERNOVA "GUEST STAR"
OF A.D. 1054

SCALE OF LIGHT-YEARS

of this holocaust is still vividly evident in the famous Crab Nebula of Taurus, a luminous space cloud which looks like an explosion to this day and has been measured to be about 4,000 light-years away, five light-years in diameter and still slowly expanding at 680 miles a second.

Among the possible causes of supernovae, one that has been discussed a good deal is the hypothesis that they are set off by collisions between stars. While such a dramatic happening could well burst the rind of helium just under the surface of either or both stars, releasing catastrophic amounts of radiation from the extremely hot interiors, calculation shows that it could not happen anywhere nearly often enough to account for the two or three supernovae known to occur on the average in each galaxy each millennium. Thus the famous "dark-star menace," which in popular imagination used to threaten the end of the world almost without warning any time, was effectively dispatched by Sir James Jeans, who estimated that the stars are so far apart there would be only one prospect of the sun's hitting another star in 600,000,000,-000,000,000 years. As most of those scientists who think the universe had a beginning place it at about 6,000,000,000 to 10,000,-000,000 years ago, we could expect only one or two collisions per 100,000,000 suns since the dawn of creation, which works out to only one crash in the whole Milky Way each 2,000,000 years — quite a modest enough batting average to soothe most anybody's jitters.

Although supernovae thus can be expected about ten thousand times as often as stellar collisions, they are rare enough not to be a source of worry and besides, any near ones will doubtless give us millions of years of forewarning once their probable atomic causes are well understood. On the credit side there are many possible benefits that may come from supernovae: one being the use of remote supernovae as milestones in gauging the distances of galaxies too far away for seeing Cepheid-variable stars. Another benefit, revealed by spectroscopic study of the Crab Nebula among others, would be the scattering (if not the creation) of the atoms of heavier elements like iron and nickel forged in supernova explosions — which some astronomers now think are just what makes possible the spawning of such dense planets as the earth or which, in any case, certainly add immeasurably to the complexity and variety of the raw material of stars in general.

Speaking of starbirth, although a celestial blessed event is veiled in far more obscurity than even its human counterpart, probably occurring nowhere but deep in the densest space clouds, something was discovered recently that happened 1,600 years ago in the potent Orion Nebula and may be the birth of two stars. A photograph taken in 1954 of a certain small region of the great cloud showed two stars that were not visible in a similar picture taken in 1947. The two apparently newborn babies have been tentatively classified as of the so-called T Tauri type, named after a famous variable in the Bull constellation and thought to be in the squirmy, nebulous condition of stellar infancy. Then, before anyone had gotten around to weighing and checking the youngsters, a similar newborn star known as R. Monocerotis in the adjoining constellation of the Unicorn was noticed in 1966 to be surrounded with clouds apparently in the actual process of coagulating into planets — a dramatic corroboration of the Kant-Laplace theory (page 153).

Aside from their behavior and dimensions, perhaps the most remarkable differences between any two stars are those revealed by their colors, which after all are but natural symptoms of their temperature and stage of incandescence. The range in our neighborhood stretches all the way from purple Pleione to ruby-red Beta Pegasi and the famous cool red giants Betelgeuse and Antares, flanked by pale rose-tinted Aldebaran or the garnet of Mu Cephei. Bluest of the blue might be Alnilam, or the potent sapphire of Rigel or hot Spica. Green: emeraldine Beta Librae or Castor or the small companion of Antares. Yellow: twinkling Albireo, golden Arcturus, or the jacinth of Capella, if not our sun. White: the diamond dog-star Sirius or dazzling Vega or doughty Deneb. If we'd include an orange star, it might be Beta Capricorni. And there are invisible infra-red ones like the supergiant of Epsilon Aurigae I and semivisible ultra-violet ones like exuberant Zeta Puppis and little Gamma Velorum of the Wolf-Rayet type. To say nothing of innumerable combinations like the carnelian and emerald revolving around each other called Gamma Andromedae, the contrasting blue and gold binary, RW Persei, or the violet and topaz Siamese twins, Beta Lyrae.

Although many of these colors appear so pale you can hardly decide whether they have any tint at all, and some are noticeably changing, they outline the vast order of stellar relationships that astronomers have been laboriously piecing together out of the apparent chaos of the skies. The now generally accepted classification of stars grew out of an idea that came into the mind of Walter Baade at Mount Wilson Observatory in 1943, when he discovered that many distant regions of the sky contain much higher percentages of giant red stars than exist around here and started working out the basic stellar relationships between age, size, temperature and color. Eventually he sorted all known members of the heavens into five main populations, as follows: Population 1, the oldest stars, particularly dim and dying dwarfs and the cool red giants like Antares, mostly to be found in remote globular clusters that swarm around the dust-free outskirts of the galaxies; Population 2, elderly and less remote stars, probably including many variables and unstable ones such as novae; Population 3, the great middle-aged majority of stars like the sun, inhabiting most of most types of spiral galaxies; Population 4, younger stars, such as Sirius, located near the nourishing, dusty central planes of galaxies; and Population 5, infant bluish stars, like hot Rigel, along with the still unborn star babies that have yet to emerge from the space clouds that spawned them.

The theoretical explanations behind such star classifications developed out of the new nuclear physics, which gives us our first real insight into stellar evolution. All stars, now explain the physicists, burn fairly steadily in their youth and early middle age like our sun, bigger ones at a faster rate, smaller ones proportionately slower, until they have used up about 15 percent of their hydrogen. Then they start to express themselves individually. Like people whose "life begins at forty," the larger ones increase their already fast pace, becoming dazzling blue giants to burn themselves out before they are much past their prime. These spendthrift stars usually turn out to be inhabitants of galactic arms, where nourishing dust clouds favor rapid growth. Smaller, slower-starting ones, however, as if to demonstrate their contrary theory that life begins after fifty, launch even more spectacular careers in their old age. Gradually increasing their rate of spending hydrogen, they swell up to 50 or 100 times their original size, thereby cooling off and becoming red giants. When their hydrogen is 60 percent gone, their internal pressure begins to drop, letting them shrink in an uneven, unstable way that often produces pulsations, irregular variability, perhaps eventually a nova splurge of greater or lesser degree before they finally collapse with their last hydrogen into the form of a dense white dwarf to fade quietly out of sight for good.

This sort of thing now appears to be going on constantly and continuously all over the sky and expresses the first reasonable cycle of life that man has been able to divine for the world of stars after countless centuries of looking and wondering and theorizing. It is a significant breakthrough into a macrocosmic existence that had long been considered hopelessly beyond human reach. For stars until quite recently were no more distinguishable one from another than water droplets in a cloud, and their motions had almost no recognizable pattern. But now we have also projected our consciousness right into their family lives by an ingenious mathematical condensation of the time dimension, so that you can see synthetic time-lapse movies of stars based on their calculated courses in which all motion is speeded up by a factor of many billions, bringing the heavens to life as vividly as fireflies on a summer night. It is a God's-eye view of the firmament with binary star couples and lively trios moving about like dancers on a ballroom floor. Globular clusters of thousands of stars show the

movements of individual members as clearly as swarming bees, each one following his own graceful orbit, often moving alternately inward and outward from the central blaze or spiraling devotedly around it under the complex druglike influence of gravity. One would think on first glance that the stars in the dazzling center of such a cluster must be actually stuck together in a contiguous fiery mass, yet the telescope discloses there is so much space between even the most densely packed stars that any of them can have dozens of planets and that it would take light a full year to reach from each to the next.

♎︎   ♏︎   ♐︎   ♑︎   ♒︎   ♓︎

Thus the lessons of perspective in the great outer world around us, the heavens that no stretch of earthbound thinking can hope to comprehend — the world of worlds in which even our seemingly immutable signs of the zodiac represent but a fleeting local viewpoint! For Libra and Aquarius are at most but finite earthly illusions. They cannot but look a little different even today as viewed from near-by Procyon and will surely look a little different again from Earth in every coming millennium. Simple projection of known star motions shows that in less than 25,000 years our fat Great Bear will have turned into a lanky giraffe, Sagittarius' quiver will be empty and Orion will have lost his belt if not his trousers. While these ideological symbols, of course, are only small twigs on the celestial family tree, they contain fertile seeds that will bloom and bear and bloom again as the world matures through future ages. Could there be any example better than Virgo, chaste deity of the equatorial sky, who carries greater secrets than the ancients could have guessed? For known even now only to the ravenous eyes and antennas of the great telescopes is a famous field of thousands of galaxies hidden in her inscrutable womb — actually the densest concentration of these potent "island universes" within fifty million light-years of here, even though admittedly but a sampling of the untold billions that drift beyond and all around them, filling every cranny of visibility in the growing seeable cosmos.

8. the foreign galaxies

BEFORE I CAME OUT INTO SPACE, I assumed that the drastic shift in perspective would do something for my mind and imagination, if not my soul. But I had little inkling of how deeply the mystery of distance would affect me up here, or of how moved I would be by the relentless presence of these worlds and worlds-of-worlds strewn all around us, above, below and on every side.

Yet the shock of space awareness here has been different only in degree from the lesser shock inflicted upon nearly every thinking man on Earth by the doings of the rocket engineers and, even more profoundly, of the astronomers. Certainly to all of us who grew up supposing the sun the brightest light in the world, it has been a jolting and humbling experience to discover instead that the great sun is really only a street lamp in a suburb of a large star city. Then that the city in turn is but a shiny grain of sand on the shores of a vast ocean of unknown extent which, for all its size, has turned out to be less than a drop of dew in a much greater continent of reality.

But that is just the sort of progressive revelation that the unfolding horizons of modern astronomy have been bringing to all mankind. And one's awakening to the galaxies and to the uncountable swarms of galaxies naturally makes one wonder: is the arrangement of the heavens a majestic example of chance, or is there really some sort of pattern signifying an over-all system behind the appalling array?

Of the latter there can hardly be any doubt, as has been intuitively sensed from the earliest times and scientifically established by measurements of increasing scope and variety ever since. For from the ancient astronomical Tables of Tirvalore in India to the 200-inch reflector of Palomar, order has prevailed in man's view of the firmament, albeit a subjective order at first — the plausible incorporation of noble figures into the zodiac, with here and there a sinuous reptile called Hydra or Draco slipped in to swallow the scattered misfit stars, and for a long period an original theory (probably conceived in India) that both Earth and sky were invisibly held up by a mystic herd of elephants upon the back of a giant tortoise, which stood on a star-spangled serpent. Such a celestial team evidently seemed both necessary and natural to ancient minds, and it was only when some genius or jester asked "What holds up the serpent?" that the philosophers got to work on profounder hypotheses of cosmology.

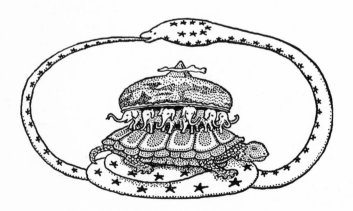

When their stirred imaginations finally accepted Tycho Brahe's ritual of systematic observation, progress seems to have naturally entered its present acceleration, the pool of known facts to have begun to expand more rapidly and measurements to take on sharper precision. Where Hipparchos and Ptolemy considered it an achievement to measure angles as fine as 5' (one sixth of the moon's diameter as seen from Earth, a twelfth of a degree), Tycho, the last great naked-eye astronomer, got it down to 10", thirty times more precise, and by the end of the nineteenth century astronomers had subdivided angles as small as 0".001, one thousandth of a second of arc or the width of a penny from two thousand miles away. Today at Palomar they are pushing 0".00001, with the big mirror polished to a tolerance of a millionth of an inch and rotating with its giant tube like a balance wheel in a Swiss watch that is comparable in size to an ocean tramp steamer.

THE RADIO TELESCOPE

Radioastronomy has blossomed even more suddenly into a major branch of the star sciences, having sprung up out of the discovery of radiation from the Milky Way as late as 1932 by Karl Jansky of the Bell Telephone Laboratories. Although at first star images "seen" by radio were much too vague to reveal which stars were sending them, the introduction of radar in World War II stimulated the development of steerable parabolic reflectors up to hundreds of feet in diameter in many countries, and even bigger interferometers in which linked antennas miles apart are tuned to the same radio source in the sky, so that its waves, arriving at slightly different times, interfere with each other in patterns that more sharply define the position of the source. Taking advantage of the fact that hydrogen in space naturally radiates energy on a wave length of 21 centimeters, the new breed of radioastronomers is now at work measuring the shapes, speeds and courses of the clouds of hydrogen in the Milky Way and beyond it and in general supplementing the optic astronomers, who are often frustrated by the dust that blocks off the light they need.

It has been estimated that more than 99 percent of our Milky Way galaxy is actually hidden behind these mysterious dust clouds. Some of them appear black like the famous Coal Sacks of Cygnus and the Southern Cross or the mysterious Elephant's Trunk cloud. Others are glowing white in reflected starlight like the great stormy Orion Nebula in the middle of the Nimrod's sword, which is probably in the act of giving birth to a new star cluster. Some have strange shapes like the Horse's Head Nebula of cold dark dust being squeezed by hot glowing gas, or the Ring Nebula illuminated by a bright star, the Rosette, the Dumbbell, the Trifid, the Owl, or the beautiful Veil in Cygnus whose fine filaments (100,000,000,000 miles thick) are thought to be jetsam from an ancient supernova still drifting through the rarefied interstellar gas. There is even a mysterious, barely visible, broadcasting cloud in Cassiopeia that was once called a "radio star" and is the strongest source of radio waves in the Milky Way, but of which almost nothing is known except the spectroscopic revelation that it is "an irregular cloud of gas with violent internal motions and high excitations," very likely including unimaginably vast cosmic thunderstorms that require centuries to discharge their equivalent of lightning from positive to negative centers of static potential. And there must be still less noticeable clouds of interacting dust and gas similar to any or all of these, which form Taurus' mane about the Pleiades and feed our sun's corona and in general compose the basic surround of galactic space, the milt of stars — being altogether a much greater thing in the sky than is commonly realized because of their preponderant invisibility.

Yet enough of the Milky Way has remained unobscured for it to have commanded attention from earliest times as the most extensive phenomenon in the visible heavens — the mysterious "Great Serpent" of the Akkadians, the "Night Manna" of the Egyptians, who believed Isis sowed it with grains of wheat, and known variously to others as "the Sky River," "Stream of the Shepherd's Hut," "River of the Divine Lady" and "Jacob's Road." Anaxagoras in 550 B.C. intuitively referred to it as "that shining wheel, men call it milk," for Greek mythology had attributed it to the milk spilled from Hera's breasts after she had angrily jerked away from the bastard Hercules, who had suckled her in her sleep. Later Greeks were to know it as "the Circle of the Galaxy," after *gala* (milk), and Romans "the Via Lactea" or Milk Run to Heaven which the departed could enter at Gemini and, if they made their way successfully, leave finally through the Door of Sagittarius, somewhere beyond which must begin the Elysian fields.

Even the Orientals and aborigine Americans seem to have independently accepted this girdle of stars as a divine pathway. The Japanese named it "the Silver River of Heaven" over which on the seventh day of their seventh month the celestial shepherd boy (Altair) and his spinning maiden (Vega) meet each year upon an invisible bridge, and the Iroquois Indians called it the "Road of Souls." The Ottawa Indians, however, considered it the wake of a divine turtle swimming along the bottom of the sky, and the Patagonians believed it the heavenly trail on which their worthy dead friends were enjoying an eternal rhea hunt, while in the Punjab it was the wake of an ark, the African bushmen knew it as "the Path of Glowing Ashes" and the early Britons unaccountably dubbed it "Watling Street."

Aristotle gave a learned scientific explanation of this hazy band as "glowing vapor," but it was Pythagoras whose earlier intuition had seen it, possibly for the first time on Earth, as "a vast assemblage of very distant stars" — stars that could only be confirmed as actually existing more than two thousand years later when Galileo finally turned his telescope upon them.

The present view of the Milky Way is changing so rapidly that it is hard to keep up with either the new evidence or the new interpretations, but the body of well-established facts has also produced quite a vivid and understandable picture that every modern education should include. In it our home galaxy is revealed as a discus-shaped mass of two hundred billion stars spinning in a turbulent whirl of gas and dust, its fiery center hidden from our optical view by the intervening shrouds, although the outer silhouette can be seen edge on fairly clearly in the faint form of the Milky Way.

The reason we view it edgewise as this dense band of myriad suns is that our own little sun happens to be near the outer rim of the great disk, whose center is hidden directly behind the faint constellation we know as Sagittarius in the southern summer sky. When you gaze in any direction other than toward the Milky Way, naturally you see practically nothing of our galaxy for you are looking axlewise or perpendicular to its plane through only part of its thickness, or a mere 5,000 light-years of distance, containing scarcely 100,000 of its stars in your general line of sight, only a few hundred of which could be visible without a telescope. But your spokewise, rim-eye view along the plane of the Milky wheel, especially when directed toward its hub in Sagittarius, exposes your eye to a thousand times more stars, one behind another for 80,-000 light-years, so that even though most of them are dimmed out by dust or made unresolvable with distance and lack of angular separation, their combined light overwhelms the intervening void with the glow of unimaginable glory that has been on its way to your eyes since before the last ice age.

If that soft flush of milkiness is still hard to visualize as a whirlpool of rampant suns, remember that its violence is on a time scale unknowable to human minds except through the abstraction of celestial mathematics and that the eye is a poor instrument for viewing it even with the aid of a telescope. In fact, were it not for radio telescopy, infra-red photography, spectroscopy and the difficult construction of deductions from such remote clues as our sister galaxy in Andromeda (a million and a half light-years beyond our own and the most remote thing visible to the naked eye), we would know hardly anything about the Milky Way, and its many spiral arms would be little more than confused clouds without demonstrable pattern or meaning.

As it is, however, we have already patched together a pretty complete model and find that our sun is on the inside of about the fourth arm out from the galactic center with a couple more fainter ones still farther out, the arms being difficult to count exactly because they are wavy and often branched and crisscrossed, apparently because of their propensity for passing through each other. Although they are all formed largely of dense luminous hydrogen and dust studded with blue supergiant stars, the clouds are arranged something like beads on a necklace, and we are fortunate in being in a clear region between beads from which we can see at least the very nearest part of our galaxy: the famous North America-shaped cloud and the spawning Orion Nebula close by in the same arm as ourselves along with big blue stars like Rigel, Vega, Altair, Spica, while a giant double-star cluster in Perseus lies in the next arm outside ours and the beautiful

OUR MILKY WAY GALAXY
showing location of the sun

SUN ORION
PERSEUS ARM
CARINA CYGNUS ARM
SAGITTARIUS ARM
radio view of center

Lagoon Nebula of flailing hydrogen in the nearest arm inside. Beyond these neighbors the veils get too thick for optical vision, but the longer-waved radio telescopes "see" to the very center of the galaxy, where a vast sphere of hydrogen 10,000 light-years in diameter is whirling about much faster than the rim regions we inhabit. The radio-eye view of this galactic nucleus understandably has a radar texture to it, yet it clearly sees clouds of hydrogen turbulently puffing and spiraling out of the sphere at speeds up to 100 miles a second, while deep inside there is a mysterious doughnut ring of denser hydrogen a mere 3,000 light-years in diameter, spinning at nearly 200 miles a second and harboring so much empty space inside it in turn that it makes one think of the eye of a hurricane — even to the weird little coin-shaped eyelid of whirling hydrogen (a few hundred light-years across) in the very center.

The significance of all this is something astronomers have barely begun to guess at, but you may get an inkling of galactic dynamics in the knowledge that the arm we are in carries the sun and Earth through one revolution of the Milky Way whirlpool every 230 million years as compared with only 120 million for the stars and clouds halfway between us and the center and with still greater angular velocities for those in the nucleus itself. Such estimates are important in calculating the galaxy's centrifugal force, which obviously must balance its gravity as long as it maintains itself. Gravity in turn is a direct indication of mass, which in the case of the Milky Way thus figures out to be 70 billion times the mass of the sun, almost 98 percent of it accounted for by stars and their satellites and the remaining 2 percent largely just loose hydrogen gas. The weight of the dust particles that often cloud the gas is only a negligible percentage of the total heft of this ethereal presence in "empty" space which, thin though it is, contains at least one atom of hydrogen in its every cubic centimeter for as far as it has been measured within the galaxy. Even a billion light-years beyond the Milky Way and well removed from any galaxies or hermit stars, traces of this basic hydrogen are believed to continue, perhaps comprising in their total immensity a good deal more than half of all the matter of the universe.

The true make-up of our Milky Way galaxy, however, cannot be grasped by considering only its vast starry disk and its all-pervasive hydrogen, for a very significant part of it is the swarm of some hundred globular clusters of stars, mostly far from the disk plane and forming a loose spheroidal skeleton around the central nucleus with the disk rim as its equator. It was astronomer Harlow Shapley who first understood this skeleton and in 1918 made the boldest hypothesis since Copernicus demonstrated that the earth revolves around the sun: pointing out that the sun in turn, far from being in a central position, must be moving around the galactic nucleus like any other humble star. And he identified and located the galactic nucleus at the center of gravity of all these massive clusters that stand out like ethereal vertebrae around the Sagittarial half of the sky.

One such compact cluster more than 30,000 light-years away in Hercules is actually visible to keen unaided eyes, while several others can be fetched by ordinary binoculars. And the curious thing about these clusters — each a remote buzzing blaze of some hundred thousand cloudfree stars — is that, while they are obviously part of the galaxy and move with it, they are normally aloof enough to be regarded almost as semisatellites or separate midget galaxies in themselves, their spherical and elliptical shapes seemingly modeled on similar-looking galaxies, a million times larger and more complex, that are now known to be floating in large numbers in all the corners of far-flung foreign space.

If the globular clusters are not true satellites but part of the basic galactic structure, as is indicated by their comparable presence in the Andromeda and all other observable galaxies, there are other recently appraised clustered-star systems, remoter and a hundred times larger, that do qualify as satellites of the Milky Way. These average about 100,000 light-years off and contain some ten million stars each, which makes them a special caste of galactic moons — comparable in relative size to the moons of Jupiter and

Saturn and, as would be expected from their distance, revolving majestically around our galaxy every two billion years!

Then what about the famous Magellanic Clouds near the Southern Cross, which even in the largest telescopes look almost like pieces of the Milky Way hurled off into the void and which have recently proved to be less than twice the galactic diameter away while steadily receding at better than 100 miles a second? Could such star systems possibly be considered satellites of our home galaxy?

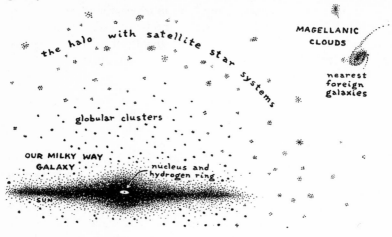

Indeed, these "Cape Clouds" of Magellan were considered just that by many astronomers after World War I when it had first become generally accepted that they were really outside the Milky Way, but during World War II it was realized that the big Cloud for certain, and probably both Clouds, are well above the average in size and mass among all galaxies in our neighborhood. The big one quite unobtrusively stretches across 30 degrees of sky. In other words, even though they may have a combined total of only twenty billion stars as against the Milky Way's two hundred billion, these Clouds are much bigger in relation to us than is any moon in relation to its planet and, since there is no evidence that they are circling around us, they are deservedly ranked as full peers among the score of members of our local clan of galaxies.

The big Cloud probably is the same "white ox" the ancient Arabs knew as *El Bakar* in their southern sky and which Anghiera, on reports from Portuguese seamen, once compared to the "mild effulgence" of the Milky Way. But it is to Pigafetta, returning years later from the famed round-the-world voyage of Magellan, that the world generally ascribes the discovery of these nearest of outside firmaments, and they have long since established themselves as symbols of alien mystery amid the exotic Antarctic constellations of *Dorado*, the goldfish; *Tucana*, the toucan; *Pavo*, the peacock; and the chameleon, phoenix, flying fish, flamingo, water serpent and bird of paradise.

And what of the rest of our local galactic gathering — who are its members and what, if anything, do they have in common? At the far end of the group is our twin, Andromeda, about ten times the distance of the Magellanic Clouds and a good ten times bigger, a great whirlpool disk tilted quarter-face to us (15 degrees from edgewise) and almost a mirror duplicate of our Milky Way though probably a little larger.

She has her similar aureole of reddish globular clusters, and the dusty clouds strung along her spiral arms are besprinkled with bluish stars. There are even two little handmaiden galaxies attending her in the manner of our Magellanic pair, although they are closer, smaller, and neatly elliptical. Then in several parts of the space between and around the two major galaxies of our clan float spiral systems of assorted sizes, three congregated at a range of 1,300,000 light-years in the constellation of Leo, others in Triangulum, Draco and the Little Bear, and four irregular dwarf galaxies of the Cape Cloud type in scattered places, with here and there half a dozen small ellipsoids. Two of the latter, called Fornax and Sculptor (after their associated constellations), are typically so low in density they are almost transparent as they drift along a cozy 400,000 light-years from us, which is less than three times the distance of the two Clouds. Evidently conforming to a general rule, about nine out of every ten local galaxies are dwarfs and vacuous to the extent that even their centers contain barely one star to each

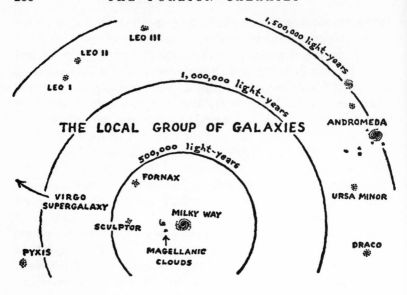

THE LOCAL GROUP OF GALAXIES

million cubic light-years of space. Several of them also are more than two million light-years away and so aloof that it is a question whether they are gravitationally tied to the rest of the family or are just strangers who happen to be passing by. There is a slight consensus of opinion, however, that the whole collection of great systems must obediently revolve around an unknown gravitational center somewhere this side of Andromeda, which, under the same influence, is now drawing toward us to the tune of 200 miles a second or just fast enough to have come a thousandth of the way during the 1,500,000 years it took her light to reach our eyes.

If this is a rough model of our own tribal stamping ground in the outer galactic cosmos, the larger picture of the knowable universe must bring in a vastly more complex and imagination-humbling pattern. Indeed, as we stretch our ken out to ten million light-years, then to 50 million, our local group containing Androm-eda and the Milky Way dwindles down to one of the smallest of a dozen widely scattered associations of galaxies. The largest is that ellipsoidal swarm of many hundreds of galaxies discovered this century centering in the direction of Virgo, and being in reality a kind of Milky Way of Milky Ways that extends (invisibly except to the most powerful of telescopes) across the entire sky edgewise for more than 120 degrees from Cepheus to Centaurus. Beyond it several other supergalaxies soon appear: one in Hydra, one occupying both Pavo and Indus and another edgewise south-ern supergalaxy mostly in Eridanus, which, exceeding that celestial river, covers about 50 degrees of sky from the larger Magellanic Cloud almost to Orion. Having now reached outward to 100 million light-years, we find a further large association of galaxies in Perseus, then a big one at 125 million in Coma Berenices and still another at 180 million in Hercules. In the next 300 million light-years beyond that, at least nine more such super organiza-

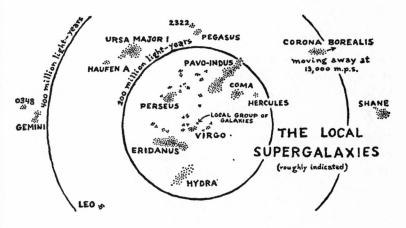

tions, each of thousands of galaxies, appear like foreign nations of the cosmos. These are usually scores of millions of light-years apart with more numerous smaller aggregations in between them and of course thousands of nomad and hermit galaxies darting about without any obvious plan.

It is hard to hold any realistic perspective in the face of such immensities. Are we ourselves perhaps part of the great Virgo nation which seems to be loosely joined to our little supergalactic tribe as to other small ones relatively near ours? There is good reason to think so, even though a substantial part of Virgo's body has been measured to be chastely receding at a brisk 700 miles a second, for Virgo as a whole is full of vital activity with differences of speed among her separate galaxies ranging to a maximum of 1,500 m.p.s., and it could well be that the Milky Way is as a corpuscle floating in a remote extremity of her vast circulation. Even the intervening gaps that at first seemed to be millions of light-years of nothing turn out to have dwarf galaxies sprinkled through them with faintly luminous filaments bridging the void from one to the next. Astrophysicist Fritz Zwicky of Palomar announced in 1952 that such intergalactic bridges, far from being exceptional, are probably the rule, and he listed hundreds of them he had already discovered, including a gracefully curved one that stretches "sharp as a lighted boulevard" for 72,-000 light-years (430 quadrillion miles)!

Gerard de Vaucouleurs, one of the French pioneers of the Virgo supergalaxy, has described this federation of Milky Ways as roughly similar to our own private Milky Way in shape and with an uncounted population of galaxies that "may run into the tens of thousands." He calculates its disk as about 40 million light-years across, by ten million thick but with much more irregularity than our Milky Way and lots of subclustering, as in the case of the "local group." There has even been measurement of rotation in its nearer parts, suggesting that its flattening, like the Milky Way's, comes from centrifugal force, and that the whole stupendous thing is one great whirlpool of whirlpools.

The alignment of our galaxy in relation to the supergalaxy is curious. It is not only closer to the rim than is the sun to the rim of the Milky Way (making our galaxy even more rural than our sun) but is turned so nearly perpendicular to it that the north pole (axial projection) of the Milky Way is found within 5 degrees of the center of the Virgo system. In other words, our galactic axis forms virtually a spoke on the super wheel, holding almost the exact opposite of the relationship that exists between the axes of Earth and sun, which are roughly parallel. It is good exercise not only for the mind but the ego thus to project our imaginations into larger and larger orientations of the sky, for we find the Copernican revelation repeated again and again — not only by Shapley, who moved the center of motion outward from sun to galaxy, but by others who have since pushed it farther to the supergalaxy and undoubtedly will continue to bear it onward step by step as man's consciousness expands indefinitely through the material cosmos.

Another way of getting a large-scale view of creation is by looking at it with a statistical eye, considering it not just as it is here or there or in any particular place but as it is everywhere on the average. This is a practical as well as hopeful approach to the largest thing we know of, because the most significant fact about averages is that they get more reliable as they are built on larger and larger numbers. Just as the risky roulette wheel can roll on to become the rock-ribbed foundation of Monte Carlo, so the apparently random irregularities of local galaxies and supergalaxies may turn into patterns of meaningful regularity if we can see them in big enough perspective.

That is exactly why several and sundry mathematicians have recently been trying out various mechanisms of chance to see what kinds of universes would result. At the Statistical Laboratory of the University of California, for instance, they began simply with a single roulette formula: divide space into equal cubes and spin the wheel once for each cube, putting a galaxy into all cubes where the wheel indicates zero and nothing into the cubes that draw any other number. But the simple universe that results from this kindergarten creation is not much like the one we see around us. Most obviously, it is too randomly scattered, showing almost nothing of the real universe's strong tendency for galaxies to be bunched in clusters.

So they tried a more complex formula. They assumed that galaxies always come in clusters, counting the occasional lone galaxies as clusters of one. Then, spinning the wheel for each cube of space as before, this time they let each zero pick a "cluster center." Thus, once the space was seeded with centers, they could spin for each center in turn to decide how many galaxies would be associated with it, and again for the galactic pattern around each center. By trying many such mechanisms and combinations of mechanisms, even adding extra steps to provide clusters of clusters, a great variety of distributions of galaxies in space could be produced. Obviously the many variables involved (such as sizes of roulette wheels, assignment and order of designations, etc.) soon become so complex that any appreciable thoroughness in covering them requires a large electronic computer, while analysis of galaxy patterns actually observed in the sky is about equally difficult. Both, of course, must be understood completely, in order to match the statistical anatomy of nature with an abstract formula of probability. This must include, among other things, an allowance for the disparity of time, since the pattern on a photographic plate of galaxies represents widely different periods of history (according to the distance traveled by the different rays of light) which must be sorted and somehow reckoned into the whole. And inevitably there must be made many such minor adjustments as the blocking of remoter galaxies by ones nearer in both space and time, the relative motion of our own galaxy, and so on.

No important breakthrough has yet been made by this weird modern approach, but the wheels are grinding and the transistors sparking over it and something will turn up sooner or later. It is surely wonderful that man's mind can probe by this abstruse method into the remote galaxies and their clusters that are lying out there upon space like handfuls of shining seed sown upon black soil. For there are actually thousands of times as many galaxies now knowable through our greatest visual and radio telescopes as all the stars ever visible to the naked eye, and each of these galaxies on the average contains literally billions of stars. What this means even in our own corner of creation can scarcely be appreciated by the calculation that if every star in our Milky Way alone had a name or a number it would take a hundred thousand fat telephone books just to list each star once. Or if someone were merely to count these stars at the rate of one per second day and night, month after weary month, the job would take more than three thousand years!

If one galaxy can be that tremendous, while its stars are trillions of miles from each to the next, how hopeless is it to grasp the infinitude of galaxies and their great tribal clusters; still more so their foreign nations. If the entire known universe were proportionately reduced to the size of the earth, for example, all its stars would disappear. For on such a scale the largest stars would be scarcely a millionth of an inch in diameter and far too small to see in any ordinary microscope. Only an electron microscope would have a chance of revealing them. And these stars would stand only a few tenths of an inch apart and a galaxy of them would be like a very faint cloud of diamond dust several hundred feet across. Outside such a galactic cloud there would be nothing but emptiness for maybe a quarter mile in all directions. Yet within another mile would appear various other clouds, perhaps flattened and tilted at odd angles to each other. If you flew through them in a fast airplane, these glittering galaxies of sub-microscopic dust would drift past you every few seconds on the average. But you would soon notice that sometimes there would be none at all for almost a whole minute, while at other times you would be virtually dazzled by a dense concentration of them, several to the second. In other words, galaxies actually live in great irregularity in the sky, and the clusters and metagalaxies (as the Milky Ways of Milky Ways are sometimes called) perhaps even more so. And you would notice all sorts of vast and wonderful patterns among these organizations of organizations of organizations as your airplane roared onward hour upon hour across the eight-thousand-mile breadth of this tiny model of the visible universe.

Of course, you would be moving much too fast to measure distance in light-years or even in the astronomer's longer units called parsecs — a parsec being the distance of a star whose direction

varies by ⅓,₆₀₀ of a degree according to whether it is viewed from
the earth or the sun, the great radius of our earth's orbit sub-
tending that tiny angle some nineteen trillion miles away, giving
such a star a parallax of exactly one second of arc at the range
of a parallax-second or parsec. Thus one parsec equals 3.26 light-
years and one light-year equals almost six trillion miles. You would
find it impractical even to use the thousand-times bigger units of
kiloparsecs and would have to resort to the million-times bigger
megaparsecs and then convert them back again in your statistical
surveys to ascertain the average number of metagalaxies per cubic
kiloparsec. As no human in the visible future is likely to move
at anything approaching such a relative speed, there remains
plenty of freedom to speculate, as does Fritz Zwicky at Palomar,
that space really "may be divided into cluster cells that fill the
universe just as bubbles fill a volume of suds."

But then one can mentally condense time as easily as space,
which brings up the question of change and evolution in these
endless but apparently fixed worlds all around us. Is there really
any kind of growth or decay in galaxies? Or metabolism of a
metagalaxy? If it takes more than two hundred million years
for the Milky Way to rotate just once, can we possibly tell its
life or say where it is going?

Yes, we can make at least a beginning of an answer, for there
are plenty of theories about this difficult question and a definite
consensus is forming. Most astrophysicists agree that the evolution of galaxies and groups of galaxies is from the diffuse and form-
less gaseous state toward condensed and complex solidity — from
simple undefined clouds of random atoms toward structural
symmetry and developed form. Weizsäcker, for instance, definitely classes all celestial objects as either clouds, rotatory forms,
or spheres, and explains in detail the sequence of development
from one to the next by means of natural forces, including
turbulence. He shows how any primordial state of uniform

distribution of matter throughout space, if indeed uniformity ever could have existed, would have had to be not only absolutely calm but paradoxically highly unstable, because as soon as the slightest irregularity or local change occurred anywhere, this prime event would inevitably have set up waves of pressure, involving gravity, radiation and magnetism, all of which are basic mediums of energy that by their nature must disperse outward, spreading what is scientifically describable as turbulence.

Obviously, this is the modern physicist's expanded version of the ancient symbolic postulate, "The earth was without form and void . . . and the Spirit of God moved upon the face of the waters." And we can safely accept turbulence as inevitable from the first event that ever happened in this eventful world, an event that could have been anything from a stupendous creative explosion to a slow condensing of uniform hydrogen. Or if you accept time as a finite illusion and events as a continuous process without beginning, then still must turbulence be ever present as one of the eternal realities of nature.

In any case, we see turbulence all around and even inside us in varying degree from the grandest reaches of space to the wind and the bile. And it may well exist inside the electron. Turbulence is the shearing effect of disparate velocities, the divergence of streams into eddies and subeddies. It is elemental dynamic form, the stress wave, the music of fluid motion. And the study of it teaches us much of how and why the diffuse gases that still permeate space have been and continuously are turning into stars and habitable worlds.

This process was already under way in the first local thickening of the primordial hydrogen, and it is ever advancing by a kind of cosmic condensation, a progressive aggregation of the gas atoms into denser regions or cells which at first are extremely nebulous and irregular, only gradually forming definite clouds. As Sir James Jeans explains it, "any gravitating gas filling a very large volume" is bound to break up into individual "gas balls." It is a phenomenon a little like the condensing of water vapor in earthly air into microscopic droplets to make the common cumulus cloud. But in the cosmic case there may be nothing as solid as dust for the gas atoms to cling to and form around. For presumably, if there was a creative beginning, there was a time before atoms had ever joined together to make dust — even before there was any such thing as a distinction between elements or a molecule or a liquid or a solid — and all these building materials of the palpable worlds had somehow to be fashioned out of raw hydrogen and its constituent parts, the simplest of all substances in the material realm.

It does not seem necessary to speculate here about the universe before the time of protons and electrons, because that pre-ionic world, if it existed, was hardly a material world at all in any understandable sense. And are we not carrying rashness far enough just to guess how hydrogen formed everything physical we have ever heard of? The mere concentration of hydrogen into regions, abetted by turbulence, could logically have produced enough pressure and eventual heat to create stars, which in turn might well have cooked up the other elements out of hydrogen particles, which by the chance and complex collisions of nature would sooner or later have made all the kinds of molecules there are. Once the heavier elements formed into solids, making dust inevitable, dense dark clouds would gather, and the assembling of planets must have started, for creation had moved into its present productive phase.

Then while stars were being condensed out of the clotting clouds in the manner already described in the chapter on the sun and the patterns of turbulence were paving the way for terrestrial life, the galaxies and great metagalaxies were likewise forming according to the dictates of turbulence. One would not suppose offhand that an eddy could be the origin of a galaxy, yet astrophysicists accept celestial eddies as the most plausible galactic source even though they know few of them last long enough to travel much farther than the length of their own diameters. In fact, as George Gamow put it, "the standard size of a galaxy would correspond to the smallest size of an eddy which can be held together by its own gravity."

Besides gravity, which we will delve deeply into in the second half of this book, there are lots of physical laws affecting the growth of star systems, such as the Kolmogoroff Law, stating that eddy speeds always vary as the cube root of their size, or the rule of Reynolds, declaring turbulence to be directly proportional to the density, width, speed and fluidity of each flow. And as irregular star clouds gradually contract under gravitation, the law of conservation of angular momentum accelerates the tempo of their turning like a spinning skater pulling in his arms, giving the clouds a more definite and symmetrical shape. This shape normally tends toward spirality with the two arms being drawn progressively closer and closer to the central body, and the great mass of star-strewn gas assuming some such double spiral as that of the Andromeda galaxy and the Milky Way. This general form prevails among a good three-quarters of all known galaxies. Weizsäcker says it happens for the same reason that cream poured into a stirred cup of coffee takes on its strikingly similar sort of dynamic symmetry, the outer parts of the cream quickly forming arms that trail behind the faster-turning center, until they are spooled into a simple ring to look like the Vincent Van Gogh–style galaxies. But as the great majority of them have arms still open and unspooled, despite the fact that some (like the Milky Way) must have already made fifty or more revolutions, astrophysicists have begun speculating that there is probably also a pinwheel effect produced by gas and stars shooting spokewise out the arms in constantly replenished streams, the strewn material later circulating axlewise back to the hub, perhaps guided by magnetic lines of force.

This hypothesis may also help to elucidate the type of open spiral that has a straight bar across its center extending for its full diameter, apparently a sort of rotary lawn sprinkler made of stars that in most cases is strewing fiery wakes behind both tips like a flaming stick thrown end over end — though just how or why a barred spiral behaves like this seems almost too much to hope to learn.

Nevertheless, in order to explain how a thin and spinning spiral galaxy might possibly evolve into a fat and sluggish ellipsoid or spherical galaxy (thirty times more massive on the average), a few theorists have suggested the spiral may somehow gradually gain mass by sucking in more material than it throws out, at the same time being braked by tidal or other friction. But again it is hardly more than a wild surmise, for human understanding of galactic evolution could be as far off the beam as a virus' judgment of human physiology — and for the same reason. Guessing the ages of great star systems millions of light-years away after less than a century of observing them is comparable to sorting children from dwarfs at first glance from the other end of a football field. What characteristics are due to age and what to inheritance? And how do you distinguish between growing and shrinking? Could not each individual galaxy have gotten that way just from the "accident" of birth, from the turbulence of its immediate surround or the magnetic breeze of a passer-by?

The vaster orders of metagalaxies and cluster continents are inevitably even less comprehensible, no doubt still far beyond reach of our growing perspective, though they are apparently galumphing grandiosely in their own unassailable largo — the giants inexorably sorting the pigmies according to cosmic hierarchies of fragmentation that accelerate as they reach smaller and smaller units — the separate members of a ten-thousand-galaxy nation often colliding and sweeping one another up like a great monopolistic industry its small competitors, even as our Milky Way may be doing with such vapid neighbors as Sculptor and Fornax.

Galactic collisions, of course, occur very frequently compared to star collisions, because galaxies on the average are only about a hundred of their own diameters apart (still closer in clusters), while stars are separated by some millions of star diameters even

THE EVOLUTION OF GALAXIES

primordial clouds of stars

loose spirals

barred spirals

tight spirals

ellipsoids

spheres

in the middle of galaxies. Yet for the same reason, galactic clashes are not very catastrophic since the meeting bodies pass right through each other like blending puffs of cigarette smoke with practically no stars ever coming within a billion miles of one another. Instead, most of the clash is between the hydrogen and other gas molecules, usually including dust clouds, which are thus swept almost completely away from large star fields. One such encounter in Perseus has turned out to be a head-on collision of a tightly spooled spiral and a large sprawling galaxy with wildly distorted arms. Another was first heard on the radio telescope as a kind of swan song from Cygnus uttered by the magnetic stress of two large galaxies that are so tightly intermeshed at present it is hardly possible to say whether either one is spiral or elliptical.

TWO GALAXIES IN PERSEUS
COLLIDING AT 2000 M.P.S.

NGC 1275

Something even more dramatic — in fact catastrophic in the extreme without being, for all we know, exactly rare — is the explosion (perhaps after implosion) of a galaxy in part or whole. Completely unknown and almost unimaginable until the 1960's, this phenomenon was discovered only in 1963 when Maarten Schmidt of Palomar Observatory, while studying what seemed to be a very faint and fuzzy thirteenth-magnitude star but one which was emitting a visible jet of matter as well as an extraordinarily strong radio signal, suddenly realized from its peculiar spectral lines that this body (known as 3C 273) must be not a star at all but something more on the order of a very remote galaxy, yet one both smaller and inexplicably a good hundred times brighter than any previously known! Thus this class of mysterious objects that astronomers had been calling "quasi-stellar radio sources" — soon to be shortened to "quasars" — suddenly attracted worldwide attention as the most astounding astronomical development since Galileo's telescope revealed the moons of Jupiter and the rings of Saturn. And that same year a remarkable photograph was taken of a somewhat similar body, this time a full-sized radio galaxy called M-82 near the Big Dipper, clearly showing its center exploding on a mind-boggling scale with streamers of hydrogen moving outward at 6,000 miles a second — no doubt gradually slowing down as they have been doing for the 1,500,000 years the outburst has taken so far. "It's equal to a million exploding stars," explained astronomer Allan Sandage, who took the picture. Then he added pensively that all radio galaxies may be exploding. Indeed galaxies of every kind may explode now and again, he said. Even our Milky Way may have exploded.

GALAXY EXPLODING

Whether all quasars are galactic explosions on a similar scale is still being debated. Quasars are believed to be the remotest bodies ever known, as well as the fastest receding: at least one of them going away at better than 82 percent of the speed of light. While bright enough to be seen at the evident range of eight billion light-years many of them flicker mysteriously, their light increasing and decreasing over periods as short as three months, which would seem impossible for anything larger than a very small group of stars. Astrophysicists trying to explain them have considered their being everything from collisions between matter and antimatter (page 486) to relatively local bodies being shot away by some tremendous recent explosion to supersupernovae that generate such immense gravitational fields that they collapse or implode inward, then explode outward with the energy of one hundred Milky Ways. The mystery continues.

The only foreseeable outcome of all this macrocosmic evolution, according to the consensus of cosmologists, is the ultimate consolidation of all matter into collapsed galaxies made up of "dead" stars, the so-called "heat death" ordained by the supposedly immutable law of entropy, under which all energy must eventually be distributed evenly everywhere, with nothing warmer or cooler than anything else and only tepid corpses of worlds floating listlessly, perhaps at greater and greater distances apart, thus rendering any encounter between them less and less possible.

White-dwarf stars like Sirius B are already practically dead and have little to look forward to but continued cooling off until they are red dwarfs and finally black ones drifting invisibly onward to an unknown future — perhaps very slowly decaying into some kind of ash or exhalation to be recirculated eventually back into the still-far-from-understood basic metabolism of the universe. It has been estimated that a good 20 percent of all stars are now in the corpse stage, buried in vacuous darkness here and there among their gay comrades even as the cemetery dwellers of earthly cities, and that the larger systems are settling into their own forms of rigor mortis. Globular clusters, for instance, may be the only remains of once-giddy young eddies of gas that condensed into spinning nebulae and eventually into small elliptical galaxies or satellites of galaxies that somehow wasted down to these cores. Gamow points out the fossil role probably played by all star systems in perpetuating the dynamic forms of primordial gas clouds, that, like pre-Cambrian seaworms, have long since been replaced by more durable solids faithfully delineating each detail of their departed bodies.

★ ∞ ★ ∞ ★

But even fossils do not last forever. Nor, for all we know, do universes of fossils. Nor perhaps even fossil universes of the third or higher orders. Which brings us to the ultimate material questions: what part of what whole is our universe? What is the over-all event that it seems to be part of? Where do space and time lead to? Is the universe resting in equilibrium, or is it going somewhere or doing something?

If you assume these questions to be beyond the scope of the human mind, you may be surprised to know that many scientists, including Einstein, have been doing solid work on them and, in the opinion of some, have already nibbled at the answers. Although we must wait until Chapter 13 before going into the basic nature of space and time, it can be said here that in the days of World War I Einstein concluded that, although a lot is obviously happening in the turbulent sky, the universe as a whole must be unchanging. In order to reach any conclusion, however, he had found it necessary to assume that gravity was opposed by a great antigravity force of repulsion, which he named the "cosmological constant" and designated by the Greek lambda, Λ, a kind of mathematical joker in the pack of eternity.

And then, only a few years later, in 1922, two major revelations convinced Einstein that cosmic repulsion was not a sound or necessary postulation after all. He frankly referred to Λ as "the biggest blunder of my life." For not only had the Russian mathematician Alexander Friedmann discovered a flaw in the jungle of equations, which might permit the theoretical "static" universe to swell or shrink despite Λ, but also Edwin Hubble, the American astronomer, had found the first observational evidence that the real universe is in fact swelling very rapidly, though not necessarily very evenly.

This Hubble did through the aforementioned doppler principle, measuring the recession of galaxies spectroscopically by the reduced pitch of their light frequency. In this remarkable way, he and his successors proved conclusively that although galaxies themselves are not measurably expanding, the distance between them is increasing on the average all over the sky. The effect of this is to find greater and greater speeds away from ourselves as we measure more and more remote galaxies, the amount being expressed by Hubble's "distance law," which says that the distance of any galaxy in millions of light-years multiplied by 105 gives its recessional velocity in miles per second. In other words, the whole known universe is literally flying apart, its outward motion approaching the velocity of light at the extreme limit of visibility and radio detection in every direction — amounting to an explosion the violence and magnitude of which could hardly begin to be suggested by a billion exploding galaxies and quasars!

Of course, it is only the scale of this cosmic phenomenon that conceals it from our earthly sense and permits us the paradox of celestial peace under "fixed" stars in a bursting universe. For galactic recession is now as accepted among astronomers as the circling of the moon about the earth. Indeed, mathematics thrives on paradoxes and can usually assimilate the implications of anything that can be measured. So the most obvious logical inference from cosmic expansion soon resulted in the hypothesis of a Belgian prelate, the Abbé Georges Lemaître, that all the receding galaxies must have once been massed together in an immensely dense primeval nucleus, a kind of unhatched egg of the universe. As developed further by Sir Arthur Eddington, Paul Adrien Maurice Dirac, George Gamow and other physicists, each cubic centimeter of such a nucleus (which Gamow calls *ylem*, from Aristotle's word for primordial substance) must have "contained at that time a hundred million tons of matter" composed mainly of photons and neutrons in an unorganized ionic state of stupendous pressure at a temperature of nearly a trillion degrees. Being a state of an assumed infinite universe, this so-called nucleus, of course, also had to be infinite in volume, and therefore cannot be imaginable as having been contained within any surface or limit. You might think of it as the manifestation of a supreme compression of endless matter, or perhaps as the peak of some cosmic wave of unimaginable dimensions that reached a node and rebounded. If time existed before the ylem, Gamow suggests calling it "Saint Augustine's era" after the man who took up the question of "what God was doing before He made heaven and earth." But it is doubted whether any material trace of such a period of prehistory could possibly have survived in any form as highly organized as hydrogen, and the survival prospect of even microscopic quantities of Augustinian heavy elements, if there ever were any, is considered less than unlikely. To put it mildly, according to the Lemaître theory the universe's material slate was wiped clean at the time of the Big Squeeze — now judged to have been roughly around the years eight to ten billion B.C., which nicely fits the well-substantiated estimate of the earth's age as close to five billion years — and we are today in a completely new cosmic generation freshly fledged and individual unto ourselves.

And the little men of the new earth, probably like beings on any planet anywhere anywhen, are trying to make what they can out of all the stimulating complexities that keep sprouting around them, including the fundamental abstract questions that obviously lurk behind the surface foliage. E. A. Milne, for instance, says the radius of the exploding universe is simply the velocity of light times its age. Dirac, for his part, has offered that the mass of the universe is the square of universal time measured in units of the interval required for a light ray to cross the diameter of an electron. And Gamow has declared that the temperature of the universe can always be approximated by dividing 25 billion degrees (F.) by the square root of the number of seconds since the day of ylem. He goes on from there to explain that although radiation was much more important (being incomparably more massive) than matter in the hot early days of the universe's explosion, by the time the universe was 250 million years old and had cooled off to an average temperature of some 150° F. below zero, the reign of radiation gave way to the reign of matter. No longer content to remain hidden and dissolved in radiation, matter at last began to condense and gravitate, and the new relative massiveness of matter was what made gravitation important and started the elaborate processes of gas concentration into clouds that ultimately spawned the stars and built the world we now know.

The wonder of all such reasoning made even Eddington confess, "The theory of the exploding universe is in some respects so preposterous that . . . I feel almost an indignation that anyone should believe it — except myself."

If looking backward from our explosion created the theory of the Big Squeeze, what can be found by looking forward? Are the receding galaxies bound to keep on accelerating with distance until they attain the speed of light and actually slip over the horizon of knowability because their radiation no longer has power to get back to us? The preponderance of thought seems to accept something of this kind as probably inevitable. And by figuring the momentum of galaxies the same way one figures the momentum of rockets fired up from the earth, it turns out that the galaxies are indeed fleeing from each other at seven times their escape velocity, which means they must have overcome intergalactic gravity by a wide margin and therefore cannot be expected ever to return together again.

The potential loophole in this calculation, of course, is that it is based on the assumption that galaxies constitute the main mass of the universe. So if the supposedly very thin hydrogen of intergalactic space should somehow prove to contain more than seven times as much mass as the galaxies, then the galaxies would not be escaping after all but would eventually slow down to a stop like a spent rocket and fall back to one another. This might produce a kind of pulsating or bouncing universe that would alternately expand and contract like a lung or a beating heart, as distinct from the so-called hyperbolic universe that must expand without limit. The latter universe, according to the "purest" mathematical requirement, must also have contracted (before the Big Squeeze) from "an infinitely thin state an eternity ago," the two sides of the Squeeze holding a mysterious mirror symmetry to each other — an implosion-explosion, involution-evolution balance that can be compared with the approach and departure of a comet and may ultimately provide the key to an understanding of time.

Still another possibility is the steady-state universe suggested first by the two English mathematicians, Hermann Bondi and Thomas Gold, then enthusiastically developed in a slightly different direction by Fred Hoyle. This theory proposes a new "cosmological principle: namely that the large-scale features of the universe are the same not only from every point of view in *space* but also from every point of view in *time*." In other words, although stars and galaxies evolve, the cosmos as a whole stays the same, its average density and energy maintaining a perfect, symmetrical equilibrium. To the question of what replaces the matter of the galaxies as they keep flying away from each other, the Bondi-Gold-Hoyle answer is: new matter is continuously and spontaneously being created everywhere at the benign rate of one atom of hydrogen in each quart of space every billion years or (which is the same thing) one atom in each cubic mile of space every hour. This creative pace was arrived at by careful calculation not only of the rate of "overflow" of matter through "the outer edge" of the expanding universe but of the rate of consumption of raw hydrogen in the condensation of primordial clouds into new galaxies. When the two rates turned out to be virtually equal, Bondi and Gold were convinced of the reality of hydrogen creation and soon began to explain the universe's expansion as an inevitable consequence of the creative pressure, while Hoyle modified the Einstein relativity equations to develop this providential interaction into a mathematical "feedback" relationship that automatically stabilizes "the mean density of matter" everywhere. The boldly postulated crea-

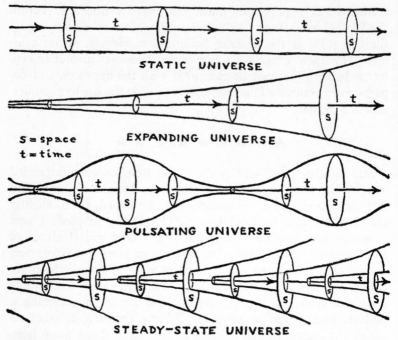

STATIC UNIVERSE

EXPANDING UNIVERSE

S = space
t = time

PULSATING UNIVERSE

STEADY-STATE UNIVERSE

SPACE-TIME RELATIONS OF THEORETICAL UNIVERSES

tion of hydrogen out of nothing has not bothered him or his colleagues a bit for, as he says, all cosmologies and philosophies require some kind of creation simply because the universe exists, and why should it be any harder to believe that hydrogen "just appears" continuously than that it was created all at once at a grand beginning eight billion years ago? Or, for that matter, why should the creation of atoms between galaxies be more mysterious than the creation of space between galaxies, which we have already accepted without undue fuss?

All things being mysterious in essence, the most serious obstacle to acceptance of the steady-state universe has turned out to be not so much its continuous creation as its dearth of evolution. For two American astronomers, Joel Stebbins and Albert Whitford, in 1948 carefully measured the reddening of light from distant galaxies through light filters of different colors and, to everyone's surprise, discovered that the light from very remote elliptical galaxies was reddened about 50 percent more than could be accounted for by the red-shift effect of recession, while the light from equally distant spiral galaxies had reddened only by the expected doppler amount, a far-from-obvious but (at the time) strongly suggestive hint of cosmic evolution.

Later this evidence was reinforced by discovery that far galaxies recede faster than proportionate to their relative distance (under the distance law) and have more frequent collisions than near galaxies, also that the remoter quasars are closer to each other than the less remote ones. The only acceptable explanation for this growing list of factors that vary in ratio to distance seems to be that we see the uttermost galaxies and quasars as they were some ten billion years ago (presumably long before either the sun or the earth was born) when they were much younger, more energetic, more numerous or crowded and more rapidly flying apart than they are today, as suggested by the comparatively moderate behavior of the nearer ones. It is even possible that quasars are long since extinct since the light and radiation arriving from the nearest and most up-to-date of them has spent something like a billion years on the way.

All such evidence of the gradual slowing down or tempering of the known universe on a grand scale of course supports the Big Squeeze (now often called Big Bang) theory and its expanding evolution in contrast to the steady-state hypothesis — to which Fred Hoyle has gamely replied that, for all anyone knows, there may be limited "bubbles" expanding and contracting here and there inside the limitless steady universe while all the galaxies and quasars we have so far become aware of just happen to be within one such locally growing bubble.

Perhaps these and similar issues relating to the tangible cosmos may remain unresolved for a long time, but the enigma of what lies beyond all sight and radio detection or any kind of physical measurement is even more profound, for it deals with a world entirely beyond the sensible — undoubtedly to a great but unknown extent beyond the capacity of the human mind. We can imagine that, when electronic amplification is perfected and applied to great telescopes erected up here on space stations well above air, galaxies farther than ten billion light-years away will come within visual range. But, according to extrapolation of the distance law, if they were ten billion light-years away when their light started toward us they would have to be more than twenty billion light-years away now (assuming they still exist as part of the material universe) and receding at more than the speed of light, which the accepted theory of relativity says no material object can do. So even visible objects, just by drifting along, may become only imaginary before their visibility is manifest. And anything any farther off might easily miss even being thought of!

As for the question of whether our universe is a closed system contained within any kind of material limits at all (perhaps what

THE BASIC GEOMETRY OF FINITE WORLDS

number of dimensions	bounded	unbounded
1	a line that ends	an endless line
2	a flat plane	closed surface
3	a volume	an endless volume

geometricians call finite but unbounded) or whether it is in some geometric sense truly infinite — with a horizon but not an end — that is the kind of abstraction Einstein took on in his general theory of relativity, which deals with the curvature of space and helps modern cosmologists in their search for evidence as to whether our universe curves positively and finitely inward like a sphere or negatively outward like an infinite saddle. But we must hold off most of this abstruse and tantalizing subject until Chapter 13.

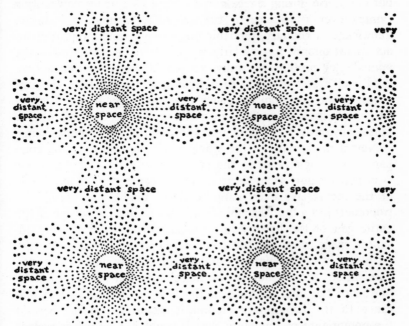

ONE MODEL OF THE ULTIMATE GRAIN OF THE UNIVERSE

Suffice it to say here that nature seems deliberately to be forcing upon us the doctrine of mysticism. For we appear to have been endowed only with finite minds that conceive of neither an end to space nor of space without end. In essence, we have been planted like seeds of blind faith in the midst of a basically nourishing medium that is nevertheless, to our present capacity, inconceivable.

Under such circumstances, it would seem arrogant in the extreme to let ourselves think we had seen or dreamed of even one millionth of one percent of the scope of all that lies around us. As every mathematician knows, the smallest percentage of infinity is still infinity. So how can we pretend to speak learnedly of the universe? Or think of astronomy as an exact science?

From where I drift, astronomy in the large is no more predictable than a card game, no more exact than a horse-race. It only seems exact in the narrow view. If you actually picked out one horse during a race and analyzed its gait by slow-motion camera over a distance of twenty yards, without any further knowledge of the race, probably horse-racing would appear as exact as astronomy is popularly supposed to be. By timing the animal's leg motions carefully, you could predict within a hundredth of a second when each hoof would next strike the turf — just as the astronomer predicts an eclipse. But if your perspective never took in more than a few cycles of the gait of one horse, obviously you would not know much about horse-racing.

Now a metagalaxy or the whole visible universe can be compared to a single horse in the race — or to a hoof of that horse — or perhaps only to an electron in a molecule in the hoof. Study of the metagalaxy over many centuries might give earthly astronomers just a hint that there was a hoof. But knowledge of the entire gait of the horse would probably have to await very advanced space travel and telescopic development beyond our wildest plans, to say nothing of hundreds of millenniums of recorded observation. Conception of the horse's position relative to other horses, of the final outcome of the race or of the race's significance to the community around it would be so far beyond the potentiality of humanity that it could not be considered of our world. Only some ultimate synthesis of soul knowledge could pronounce the winner or begin to comprehend the reaction of the inconceivable public at large.

As it takes perspective to gain perspective, it will be a long bootstrap climb upward from man's present celestial outlook to one as relatively comprehending as that of a baby attending the circus. Indeed, the frankest acceptance of modern cosmology's limitations is vital to our progress through this firmament paved and ceiled with mystery from before the eldest dawn until long after the youngest night, from higher than the zenith to lower than the nadir, even from far far beyond all the horizons of radiation or gravity or thought.

Ylem and self-seeding hydrogen and every other swig of the Bacchanalia of current cosmic hypotheses seems to me to suffer from an insufficient allowance for the unknown — for the limitless complex of possibilities beyond measurement or sense. In actual fact, why could not the universe be expanding just because eternity is nonsymmetrical? Or because what we see is only part of some great supercosmic bubble that is unaccountably in ferment, perhaps literally an eddy of some much vaster turbulence or willfulness? Or maybe even an ingredient in the outer dynamic equivalent of a stew or a storm or a web or a wish in the unknowable macrocosm? After all, the wagon wheel feels only one small part of the road. Yet all the road is there.

Far from a depressing thought, this enhumbling of the known is relatively and really an enlargement of the whole and an enhancement of our total potentiality. For "day unto day uttereth speech and night unto night sheweth knowledge," and the wisdom of the stars is the wisdom of man who, in spite of himself, is indirectly but materially made of stars. Even man's glorious going forth into space is as nothing to the greater glory of space's coming to man in return — to acquaint him with "the ordinances of heaven" that, better than Job, he may someday "set the dominion thereof in the earth" and in all habitable creation.

CATALOGUE OF DOVER BOOKS

Art, History of Art, Antiques, Graphic Arts, Handcrafts

ART STUDENTS' ANATOMY, E. J. Farris. Outstanding art anatomy that uses chiefly living objects for its illustrations. 71 photos of undraped men, women, children are accompanied by carefully labeled matching sketches to illustrate the skeletal system, articulations and movements, bony landmarks, the muscular system, skin, fasciae, fat, etc. 9 x-ray photos show movement of joints. Undraped models are shown in such actions as serving in tennis, drawing a bow in archery, playing football, dancing, preparing to spring and to dive. Also discussed and illustrated are proportions, age and sex differences, the anatomy of the smile, etc. 8 plates by the great early 18th century anatomic illustrator Siegfried Albinus are also included. Glossary. 158 figures, 7 in color. x + 159pp. 5⅝ x 8⅜.   T744 Paperbound **$1.50**

AN ATLAS OF ANATOMY FOR ARTISTS, F Schider. A new 3rd edition of this standard text enlarged by 52 new illustrations of hands, anatomical studies by Cloquet, and expressive life studies of the body by Barcsay. 189 clear, detailed plates offer you precise information of impeccable accuracy. 29 plates show all aspects of the skeleton, with closeups of special areas, while 54 full-page plates, mostly in two colors, give human musculature as seen from four different points of view, with cutaways for important portions of the body. 14 full-page plates provide photographs of hand forms, eyelids, female breasts, and indicate the location of muscles upon models. 59 additional plates show how great artists of the past utilized human anatomy. They reproduce sketches and finished work by such artists as Michelangelo, Leonardo da Vinci, Goya, and 15 others. This is a lifetime reference work which will be one of the most important books in any artist's library. "The standard reference tool," AMERICAN LIBRARY ASSOCIATION. "Excellent," AMERICAN ARTIST. Third enlarged edition. 189 plates, 647 illustrations. xxvi + 192pp. 7⅞ x 10⅝.   T241 Clothbound **$6.00**

AN ATLAS OF ANIMAL ANATOMY FOR ARTISTS, W. Ellenberger, H. Baum, H. Dittrich. The largest, richest animal anatomy for artists available in English. 99 detailed anatomical plates of such animals as the horse, dog, cat, lion, deer, seal, kangaroo, flying squirrel, cow, bull, goat, monkey, hare, and bat. Surface features are clearly indicated, while progressive beneath-the-skin pictures show musculature, tendons, and bone structure. Rest and action are exhibited in terms of musculature and skeletal structure and detailed cross-sections are given for heads and important features. The animals chosen are representative of specific families so that a study of these anatomies will provide knowledge of hundreds of related species. "Highly recommended as one of the very few books on the subject worthy of being used as an authoritative guide," DESIGN. "Gives a fundamental knowledge," AMERICAN ARTIST. Second revised, enlarged edition with new plates from Cuvier, Stubbs, etc. 288 illustrations. 153pp. 11⅜ x 9.   T82 Clothbound **$6.00**

THE HUMAN FIGURE IN MOTION, Eadweard Muybridge. The largest selection in print of Muybridge's famous high-speed action photos of the human figure in motion. 4789 photographs illustrate 162 different actions: men, women, children—mostly undraped—are shown walking, running, carrying various objects, sitting, lying down, climbing, throwing, arising, and performing over 150 other actions. Some actions are shown in as many as 150 photographs each. All in all there are more than 500 action strips in this enormous volume, series shots taken at shutter speeds of as high as 1/6000th of a second! These are not posed shots, but true stopped motion. They show bone and muscle in situations that the human eye is not fast enough to capture. Earlier, smaller editions of these prints have brought $40 and more on the out-of-print market. "A must for artists," ART IN FOCUS. "An unparalleled dictionary of action for all artists," AMERICAN ARTIST. 390 full-page plates, with 4789 photographs. Printed on heavy glossy stock. Reinforced binding with headbands. xxi + 390pp. 7⅞ x 10⅝.   T204 Clothbound **$10.00**

ANIMALS IN MOTION, Eadweard Muybridge. This is the largest collection of animal action photos in print. 34 different animals (horses, mules, oxen, goats, camels, pigs, cats, guanacos, lions, gnus, deer, monkeys, eagles—and 21 others) in 132 characteristic actions. The horse alone is shown in more than 40 different actions. All 3919 photographs are taken in series at speeds up to 1/6000th of a second. The secrets of leg motion, spinal patterns, head movements, strains and contortions shown nowhere else are captured. You will see exactly how a lion sets his foot down; how an elephant's knees are like a human's—and how they differ; the position of a kangaroo's legs in mid-leap; how an ostrich's head bobs; details of the flight of birds—and thousands of facets of motion only the fastest cameras can catch. Photographed from domestic animals and animals in the Philadelphia zoo, it contains neither semiposed artificial shots nor distorted telephoto shots taken under adverse conditions. Artists, biologists, decorators, cartoonists, will find this book indispensable for understanding animals in motion. "A really marvelous series of plates," NATURE (London). "The dry plate's most spectacular early use was by Eadweard Muybridge," LIFE. 3919 photographs; 380 full pages of plates. 440pp. Printed on heavy glossy paper. Deluxe binding with headbands. 7⅞ x 10⅝.   T203 Clothbound **$10.00**

ART ANATOMY, William Rimmer, M.D. Often called one of America's foremost contributions to art instruction, a work of art in its own right. More than 700 line drawings by the author, first-rate anatomist and dissector as well as artist, with a non-technical anatomical text. Impeccably accurate drawings of muscles, skeletal structure, surface features, other aspects of males and females, children, adults and aged persons show not only form, size, insertion and articulation but personality and emotion as reflected by physical features usually ignored in modern anatomical works. Complete unabridged reproduction of 1876 edition slightly rearranged. Introduction by Robert Hutchinson. 722 illustrations. xiii + 153pp. 7¾ x 10¾.
T908 Paperbound **$2.00**

ANIMAL DRAWING: ANATOMY AND ACTION FOR ARTISTS, C. R. Knight. The author and illustrator of this work was "the most distinguished painter of animal life." This extensive course in animal drawing discusses musculature, bone structure, animal psychology, movements, habits, habitats. Innumerable tips on proportions, light and shadow play, coloring, hair formation, feather arrangement, scales, how animals lie down, animal expressions, etc., from great apes to birds. Pointers on avoiding gracelessness in horses, deer; on introducing proper power and bulk to heavier animals; on giving proper grace and subtle expression to members of the cat family. Originally titled "Animal Anatomy and Psychology for the Artist and Layman." Over 123 illustrations. 149pp. 8¼ x 10½.
T426 Paperbound **$2.00**

DESIGN FOR ARTISTS AND CRAFTSMEN, L. Wolchonok. The most thorough course ever prepared on the creation of art motifs and designs. It teaches you to create your own designs out of things around you — from geometric patterns, plants, birds, animals, humans, landscapes, and man-made objects. It leads you step by step through the creation of more than 1300 designs, and shows you how to create design that is fresh, well-founded, and original. Mr. Wolchonok, whose text is used by scores of art schools, shows you how the same idea can be developed into many different forms, ranging from near representationalism to the most advanced forms of abstraction. The material in this book is entirely new, and combines full awareness of traditional design with the work of such men as Miro, Léger, Picasso, Moore, and others. 113 detailed exercises, with instruction hints, diagrams, and details to enable you to apply Wolchonok's methods to your own work. "A great contribution to the field of design and crafts," N. Y. SOCIETY OF CRAFTSMEN. More than 1300 illustrations. xv + 207pp. 7⅞ x 10¾.
T274 Clothbound **$4.95**

HAWTHORNE ON PAINTING. A vivid recreation, from students' notes, of instruction by Charles W. Hawthorne, given for over 31 years at his famous Cape Cod School of Art. Divided into sections on the outdoor model, still life, landscape, the indoor model, and water color, each section begins with a concise essay, followed by epigrammatic comments on color, form, seeing, etc. Not a formal course, but comments of a great teacher-painter on specific student works, which will solve problems in your own painting and understanding of art. "An excellent introduction for laymen and students alike," Time. Introduction. 100pp. 5⅜ x 8.
T653 Paperbound **$1.00**

THE ENJOYMENT AND USE OF COLOR, Walter Sargent. This book explains fascinating relations among colors, between colors in nature and art; describes experiments that you can perform to understand these relations more thoroughly; points out hundreds of little known facts about color values, intensities, effects of high and low illumination, complementary colors, color harmonies. Practical hints for painters, references to techniques of masters, questions at chapter ends for self-testing all make this a valuable book for artists, professional and amateur, and for general readers interested in world of color. Republication of 1923 edition. 35 illustrations, 6 full-page plates. New color frontispiece. Index. xii + 274pp. 5⅜ x 8.
T944 Paperbound **$2.25**

DECORATIVE ALPHABETS AND INITIALS, ed. by Alexander Nesbitt. No payment, no permission needed to reproduce any one of these 3924 different letters, covering 1000 years. Crisp, clear letters all in line, from Anglo-Saxon mss., Luebeck Cathedral, 15th century Augsburg; the work of Dürer, Holbein, Cresci, Beardsley, Rossing Wadsworth, John Moylin, etc. Every imaginable style. 91 complete alphabets. 123 full-page plates. 192pp. 7¾ x 10¾.
T544 Paperbound **$2.25**

THREE CLASSICS OF ITALIAN CALLIGRAPHY, edited by Oscar Ogg. Here, combined in a single volume, are complete reproductions of three famous calligraphic works written by the greatest writing masters of the Renaissance: Arrighi's OPERINA and IL MODO, Tagliente's LO PRESENTE LIBRO, and Palatino's LIBRO NUOVO. These books present more than 200 complete alphabets and thousands of lettered specimens. The basic hand is Papal Chancery, but scores of other alphabets are also given: European and Asiatic local alphabets, foliated and art alphabets, scrolls, cartouches, borders, etc. Text is in Italian. Introduction. 245 plates. x + 272pp. 6⅛ x 9¼.
T212 Paperbound **$2.25**

CALLIGRAPHY, J. G. Schwandner. One of the legendary books in the graphic arts, copies of which brought $500 each on the rare book market, now reprinted for the first time in over 200 years. A beautiful plate book of graceful calligraphy, and an inexhaustible source of first-rate material copyright-free, for artists, and directors, craftsmen, commercial artists, etc. More than 300 ornamental initials forming 12 complete alphabets, over 150 ornate frames and panels, over 200 flourishes, over 75 calligraphic pictures including a temple, cherubs, cocks, dodos, stags, chamois, foliated lions, greyhounds, etc. Thousand of calligraphic elements to be used for suggestions of quality, sophistication, antiquity, and sheer beauty. Historical introduction. 158 full-page plates. 368pp. 9 x 13.
T475 Clothbound **$10.00**

CATALOGUE OF DOVER BOOKS

THE HISTORY AND TECHNIQUE OF LETTERING, A. Nesbitt. The only thorough inexpensive history of letter forms from the point of view of the artist. Mr. Nesbitt covers every major development in lettering from the ancient Egyptians to the present and illustrates each development with a complete alphabet. Such masters as Baskerville, Bell, Bodoni, Caslon, Koch, Kilian, Morris, Garamont, Jenson, and dozens of others are analyzed in terms of artistry and historical development. The author also presents a 65-page practical course in lettering, besides the full historical text. 89 complete alphabets; 165 additional lettered specimens. xvii + 300pp. 5⅜ x 8. **T427 Paperbound $2.00**

FOOT-HIGH LETTERS: A GUIDE TO LETTERING (A PRACTICAL SYLLABUS FOR TEACHERS), M. Price. A complete alphabet of Classic Roman letters, each a foot high, each on a separate 16 x 22 plate—perfect for use in lettering classes. In addition to an accompanying description, each plate also contains 9 two-inch-high forms of letter in various type faces, such as "Caslon," "Empire," "Onyx," and "Neuland," illustrating the many possible derivations from the standard classical forms. One plate contains 21 additional forms of the letter A. The fully illustrated 16-page syllabus by Mr. Price, formerly of the Pratt Institute and the Rhode Island School of Design, contains dozens of useful suggestions for student and teacher alike. An indispensable teaching aid. Extensively revised. 16-page syllabus and 30 plates in slip cover, 16 x 22. **T239 Clothbound $6.00**

THE STYLES OF ORNAMENT, Alexander Speltz. Largest collection of ornaments in print— 3765 illustrations of prehistoric, Lombard, Gothic, Frank, Romanesque, Mohammedan, Renaissance, Polish, Swiss, Rococo, Sheraton, Empire, U. S. Colonial, etc., ornament. Gargoyles, dragons, columns, necklaces, urns, friezes, furniture, buildings, keyholes, tapestries, fantastic animals, armor, religious objects, much more, all in line. Reproduce any one free. Index. Bibliography. 400 plates. 656pp. 5⅝ x 8⅜. **T557 Paperbound $2.50**

HANDBOOK OF DESIGNS AND DEVICES, C. P. Hornung. This unique book is indispensable to the designer, commercial artist, and hobbyist. It is not a textbook but a working collection of 1836 basic designs and variations, carefully reproduced, which may be used without permission. Variations of circle, line, band, triangle, square, cross, diamond, swastika, pentagon, octagon, hexagon, star, scroll, interlacement, shields, etc. Supplementary notes on the background and symbolism of the figures. "A necessity to every designer who would be original without having to labor heavily," ARTIST AND ADVERTISER. 204 plates. 240pp. 5⅜ x 8. **T125 Paperbound $2.00**

THE UNIVERSAL PENMAN, George Bickham. This beautiful book, which first appeared in 1743, is the largest collection of calligraphic specimens, flourishes, alphabets, and calligraphic illustrations ever published. 212 full-page plates are drawn from the work of such 18th century masters of English roundhand as Dove, Champion, Bland, and 20 others. They contain 22 complete alphabets, over 2,000 flourishes, and 122 illustrations, each drawn with a stylistic grace impossible to describe. This book is invaluable to anyone interested in the beauties of calligraphy, or to any artist, hobbyist, or craftsman who wishes to use the very best ornamental handwriting and flourishes for decorative purposes. Commercial artists, advertising artists, have found it unexcelled as a source of material suggesting quality. "An essential part of any art library, and a book of permanent value," AMERICAN ARTIST. 212 plates. 224pp. 9 x 13¾. **T20 Clothbound $10.00**

1800 WOODCUTS BY THOMAS BEWICK AND HIS SCHOOL. Prepared by Dover's editorial staff, this is the largest collection of woodcuts by Bewick and his school ever compiled. Contains the complete engravings from all his major works and a wide range of illustrations from lesser-known collections, all photographed from clear copies of the original books and reproduced in line. Carefully and conveniently organized into sections on Nature (animals and birds, scenery and landscapes, plants, insects, etc.), People (love and courtship, social life, school and domestic scenes, misfortunes, costumes, etc.), Business and Trade, and illustrations from primers, fairytales, spelling books, frontispieces, borders, fables and allegories, etc. In addition to technical proficiency and simple beauty, Bewick's work is remarkable as a mode of pictorial symbolism, reflecting rustic tranquility, an atmosphere of rest, simplicity, idyllic contentment. A delight for the eye, an inexhaustible source of illustrative material for art studios, commercial artists, advertising agencies. Individual illustrations (up to 10 for any one use) are copyright free. Classified index. Bibliography and sources. Introduction by Robert Hutchinson. 1800 woodcuts. xiv + 247pp. 9 x 12. **T766 Clothbound $10.00**

A HANDBOOK OF EARLY ADVERTISING ART, C. P. Hornung. The largest collection of copyright-free early advertising art ever compiled. Vol. I contains some 2,000 illustrations of agricultural devices, animals, old automobiles, birds, buildings, Christmas decorations (with 7 Santa Clauses by Nast), allegorical figures, fire engines, horses and vehicles, Indians, portraits, sailing ships, trains, sports, trade cuts — and 30 other categories! Vol. II, devoted to typography, has over 4000 specimens: 600 different Roman, Gothic, Barnum, Old English faces; 630 ornamental type faces; 1115 initials, hundreds of scrolls, flourishes, etc. This third edition is enlarged by 78 additional plates containing all new material. "A remarkable collection," PRINTERS' INK. "A rich contribution to the history of American design," GRAPHIS. Volume I, Pictorial. Over 2000 illustrations. xiv + 242pp. 9 x 12. **T122 Clothbound $10.00**
Volume II, Typographical. Over 4000 specimens. vii + 312pp. 9 x 12. T123 Clothbound **$10.00**
Two volume set, T121 Clothbound, only **$18.50**

THE 100 GREATEST ADVERTISEMENTS, WHO WROTE THEM AND WHAT THEY DID, J. L. Watkins.
100 (plus 13 added for this edition) of most successful ads ever to appear. "Do You Make
These Mistakes in English," "They laughed when I sat down," "A Hog Can Cross the
Country," "The Man in the Hathaway Shirt," over 100 more ads that changed habits of a
nation, gave new expressions to the language, built reputations. Also salient facts behind
ads, often in words of their creators. "Useful . . . valuable . . . enlightening," Printers' Ink.
2nd revised edition. Introduction. Foreword by Raymond Rubicam. Index. 130 illustrations.
252pp. 7¾ x 10¾. **T540 Paperbound $2.50**

**THE DIDEROT PICTORIAL ENCYCLOPEDIA OF TRADES AND INDUSTRY, MANUFACTURING AND
THE TECHNICAL ARTS IN PLATES SELECTED FROM "L'ENCYCLOPEDIE OU DICTIONNAIRE
RAISONNE DES SCIENCES, DES ARTS, ET DES METIERS" OF DENIS DIDEROT,** edited with
text by C. Gillispie. The first modern selection of plates from the high point of 18th century
French engraving, Diderot's famous Encyclopedia. Over 2000 illustrations on 485 full-page
plates, most of them original size, illustrating the trades and industries of one of the
most fascinating periods of modern history, 18th century France. These magnificent engravings provide an invaluable source of fresh, copyright-free material to artists and illustrators,
a lively and accurate social document to students of cultures, an outstanding find to the
lover of fine engravings. The plates teem with life, with men, women, and children performing
all of the thousands of operations necessary to the trades before and during the early stages
of the industrial revolution. Plates are in sequence, and show general operations, closeups of
difficult operations, and details of complex machinery. Such important and interesting trades
and industries are illustrated as sowing, harvesting, beekeeping, cheesemaking, operating
windmills, milling flour, charcoal burning, tobacco processing, indigo, fishing, arts of war,
salt extraction, mining, smelting iron, casting iron steel, extracting mercury, zinc, sulphur,
copper, etc., slating, tinning, silverplating, gilding, making gunpowder, cannons, bells,
shoeing horses, tanning, papermaking, printing, dying, and more than 40 other categories.
Besides being a work of remarkable beauty and skill, this is also one of the largest collections
of working figures in print. 920pp. 9 x 12. Heavy library cloth. **T421 Two volume set $18.50**

THE HANDBOOK OF PLANT AND FLORAL ORNAMENT, R. G. Hatton. One of the truly great collections of plant drawings for reproduction: 1200 different figures of flowering or fruiting
plants—line drawings that will reproduce excellently. Selected from superb woodcuts and
copperplate engravings appearing mostly in 16th and 17th century herbals including the
fabulously rare "Kreuter Büch" (Bock) "Cruijde Boeck" (Dodoens), etc. Plants classified according to botanical groups. Also excellent reading for anyone interested in home gardening or
any phase of horticulture. Formerly "The Craftsman's Plant-Book: or Figures of Plants."
Introductions. Over 1200 illustrations. Index. 548pp. 6⅛ x 9¼. **T649 Paperbound $3.00**

HANDBOOK OF ORNAMENT, F. S. Meyer. One of the largest collections of copyright-free traditional art in print. It contains over 3300 line cuts from Greek, Roman, Medieval, Islamic,
Renaissance, Baroque, 18th and 19th century sources. 180 plates illustrate elements of design
with networks, Gothic tracery, geometric elements, flower and animal motifs, etc., while 100
plates illustrate decorative objects: chairs, thrones, daises, cabinets, crowns, weapons,
utensils, vases, jewelry, armor, heraldry, bottles, altars, and scores of other objects. Indispensable for artists, illustrators, designers, handicrafters, etc. Full text. 3300 illustrations.
xiv + 548pp. 5⅜ x 8. **T302 Paperbound $2.50**

COSTUMES OF THE GREEKS AND ROMANS, Thomas Hope. Authentic costumes from all walks
of life in Roman, Greek civilizations, including Phrygia, Egypt, Persia, Parthia, Etruria, in
finely drawn, detailed engravings by Thomas Hope (1770-1831). Scores of additional engravings
of ancient musical instruments, furniture, jewelry, sarcophagi, other adjuncts to ancient
life. All carefully copied from ancient vases and statuary. Textual introduction by author.
Art and advertising personnel, costume and stage designers, students of fashion design will
find these copyright-free engravings a source of ideas and inspiration and a valuable reference. Republication of 1st (1812) edition. 300 full-page plates, over 700 illustrations.
xliv + 300pp. 5⅝ x 8⅜. **T21 Paperbound $2.00**

PRINCIPLES OF ART HISTORY, H. Wölfflin. Analyzing such terms as "baroque," "classic,"
"neoclassic," "primitive," "picturesque," and 164 different works by artists like Botticelli,
van Cleve, Dürer, Hobbema, Holbein, Hals, Rembrandt, Titian, Brueghel, Vermeer, and many
others, the author establishes the classifications of art history and style on a firm, concrete
basis. This classic of art criticism shows what really occurred between the 14th century
primitives and the sophistication of the 18th century in terms of basic attitudes and philosophies. "A remarkable lesson in the art of seeing," SAT. REV. OF LITERATURE. Translated from
the 7th German edition. 150 illustrations. 254pp. 6⅛ x 9¼. **T276 Paperbound $2.00**

AFRICAN SCULPTURE, Ladislas Segy. First publication of a new book by the author of critically
acclaimed AFRICAN SCULPTURE SPEAKS. It contains 163 full-page plates illustrating masks,
fertility figures, ceremonial objects, etc., representing the culture of 50 tribes of West
and Central Africa. Over 85% of these works of art have never been illustrated before, and
each is an authentic and fascinating tribal artifact. A 34-page introduction explains the
anthropological, psychological, and artistic values of African sculpture. "Mr. Segy is one of
its top authorities," NEW YORKER. 164 full-page photographic plates. Bibliography. 244pp.
6 x 9. **T396 Paperbound $2.00**

Dover Classical Records

Now available directly to the public exclusively from Dover: top-quality recordings of fine classical music for only $2 per record! Originally released by a major company (except for the previously unreleased Gimpel recording of Bach) to sell for $5 and $6, these records were issued under our imprint only after they had passed a severe critical test. We insisted upon:

First-rate music that is enjoyable, musically important and culturally significant.

First-rate performances, where the artists have carried out the composer's intentions, in which the music is alive, vigorous, played with understanding and sympathy.

First-rate sound—clear, sonorous, fully balanced, crackle-free, whir-free.

Have in your home music by major composers, performed by such gifted musicians as Elsner, Gitlis, Wührer, the Barchet Quartet, Gimpel. Enthusiastically received when first released, many of these performances are definitive. The records are not seconds or remainders, but brand new pressings made on pure vinyl from carefully chosen master tapes. "All purpose" 12" monaural 33⅓ rpm records, they play equally well on hi-fi and stereo equipment. Fine music for discriminating music lovers, superlatively played, flawlessly recorded: there is no better way to build your library of recorded classical music at remarkable savings. There are no strings; this is not a come-on, not a club, forcing you to buy records you may not want in order to get a few at a lower price. Buy whatever records you want in any quantity, and never pay more than $2 each. Your obligation ends with your first purchase. And that's when ours begins. Dover's money-back guarantee allows you to return any record for any reason, even if you don't like the music, for a full, immediate refund, no questions asked.

MOZART: STRING QUARTET IN A MAJOR (K.464); STRING QUARTET IN C MAJOR ("DISSONANT", K.465), Barchet Quartet. The final two of the famed Haydn Quartets, high-points in the history of music. The A Major was accepted with delight by Mozart's contemporaries, but the C Major, with its dissonant opening, aroused strong protest. Today, of course, the remarkable resolutions of the dissonances are recognized as major musical achievements. "Beautiful warm playing," MUSICAL AMERICA. "Two of Mozart's loveliest quartets in a distinguished performance," REV. OF RECORDED MUSIC. (Playing time 58 mins.) HCR 5200 **$2.00**

MOZART: QUARTETS IN G MAJOR (K.80); D MAJOR (K.155); G MAJOR (K.156); C MAJOR (K157), Barchet Quartet. The early chamber music of Mozart receives unfortunately little attention. First-rate music of the Italian school, it contains all the lightness and charm that belongs only to the youthful Mozart. This is currently the only separate source for the composer's work of this time period. "Excellent," HIGH FIDELITY. "Filled with sunshine and youthful joy; played with verve, recorded sound live and brilliant," CHRISTIAN SCI. MONITOR. (Playing time 51 mins.) HCR 5201 **$2.00**

MOZART: SERENADE #9 IN D MAJOR ("POSTHORN", K.320); SERENADE #6 IN D MAJOR ("SERENATA NOTTURNA", K.239), Pro Musica Orch. of Stuttgart, under Edouard van Remoortel. For Mozart, the serenade was a highly effective form, since he could bring to it the immediacy and intimacy of chamber music as well as the free fantasy of larger group music. Both these serenades are distinguished by a playful, mischievous quality, a spirit perfectly captured in this fine performance. "A triumph, polished playing from the orchestra," HI FI MUSIC AT HOME. "Sound is rich and resonant, fidelity is wonderful," REV. OF RECORDED MUSIC. (Playing time 51 mins.) HCR 5202 **$2.00**

MOZART: DIVERTIMENTO IN E FLAT MAJOR FOR STRING TRIO (K.563); ADAGIO AND FUGUE IN F MINOR FOR STRING TRIO (K.404a), Kehr Trio. The Divertimento is one of Mozart's most beloved pieces, called by Einstein "the finest, most perfect trio ever heard." It is difficult to imagine a music lover who will not be delighted by it. This is the only recording of the lesser known Adagio and Fugue, written in 1782 and influenced by Bach's Well-Tempered Clavichord. "Extremely beautiful recording, strongly recommended," THE OBSERVER. "Superior to rival editions," HIGH FIDELITY. (Playing time 51 mins.) HCR 5203 **$2.00**

SCHUMANN: KREISLERIANA (OP.16); FANTASY IN C MAJOR ("FANTASIE," OP.17), Vlado Perlemuter, Piano. The vigorous Romantic imagination and the remarkable emotional qualities of Schumann's piano music raise it to special eminence in 19th century creativity. Both these pieces are rooted to the composer's tortuous romance with his future wife, Clara, and both receive brilliant treatment at the hands of Vlado Perlemuter, Paris Conservatory, proclaimed by Alfred Cortot "not only a great virtuoso but also a great musician." "The best Kreisleriana to date," BILLBOARD. (Playing time 55 mins.) HCR 5204 **$2.00**

SCHUMANN: TRIO #1, D MINOR; TRIO #3, G MINOR, Trio di Bolzano. The fiery, romantic, melodic Trio #1, and the dramatic, seldom heard Trio #3 are both movingly played by a fine chamber ensemble. No one personified Romanticism to the general public of the 1840's more than did Robert Schumann, and among his most romantic works are these trios for cello, violin and piano. "Ensemble and overall interpretation leave little to be desired," HIGH FIDELITY. "An especially understanding performance," REV. OF RECORDED MUSIC. (Playing time 54 mins.) HCR 5205 **$2.00**

CATALOGUE OF DOVER BOOKS

SCHUMANN: TRIOS #1 IN D MINOR (OPUS 63) AND #3 IN G MINOR (OPUS 110), Trio di Bolzano. The fiery, romantic, melodic Trio #1 and the dramatic, seldom heard Trio #3 are both movingly played by a fine chamber ensemble. No one personified Romanticism to the general public of the 1840's more than did Robert Schumann, and among his most romantic works are these trios for cello, violin and piano. "Ensemble and overall interpretation leave little to be desired," HIGH FIDELITY. "An especially understanding performance," REV. OF RECORDED MUSIC. (Playing time 54 mins.)   **HCR 5205 $2.00**

SCHUBERT: QUINTET IN A ("TROUT") (OPUS 114), AND NOCTURNE IN E FLAT (OPUS 148), Friedrich Wührer, Piano and Barchet Quartet. If there is a single piece of chamber music that is a universal favorite, it is probably Schubert's "Trout" Quintet. Delightful melody, harmonic resources, musical exuberance are its characteristics. The Nocturne (played by Wührer, Barchet, and Reimann) is an exquisite piece with a deceptively simple theme and harmony. "The best Trout on the market—Wührer is a fine Viennese-style Schubertian, and his spirit infects the Barchets," ATLANTIC MONTHLY. "Exquisitely recorded," ETUDE. (Playing time 44 mins.)   **HCR 5206 $2.00**

SCHUBERT: PIANO SONATAS IN C MINOR AND B (OPUS 147), Friedrich Wührer. Schubert's sonatas retain the structure of the classical form, but delight listeners with romantic freedom and a special melodic richness. The C Minor, one of the Three Grand Sonatas, is a product of the composer's maturity. The B Major was not published until 15 years after his death. "Remarkable interpretation, reproduction of the first rank," DISQUES. "A superb pianist for music like this, musicianship, sweep, power, and an ability to integrate Schubert's measures such as few pianists have had since Schnabel," Harold Schonberg. (Playing time 49 mins.)   **HCR 5207 $2.00**

STRAVINSKY: VIOLIN CONCERTO IN D, Ivry Gitlis, Cologne Orchestra; DUO CONCERTANTE, Ivry Gitlis, Violin, Charlotte Zelka, Piano, Cologne Orchestra; JEU DE CARTES, Bamberg Symphony, under Hollreiser. Igor Stravinsky is probably the most important composer of this century, and these three works are among the most significant of his neoclassical period of the 30's. The Violin Concerto is one of the few modern classics. Jeu de Cartes, a ballet score, bubbles with gaiety, color and melodiousness. "Imaginatively played and beautifully recorded," E. T. Canby, HARPERS MAGAZINE. "Gitlis is excellent, Hollreiser beautifully worked out," HIGH FIDELITY. (Playing time 55 mins.)   **HCR 5208 $2.00**

GEMINIANI: SIX CONCERTI GROSSI, OPUS 3, Helma Elsner, Harpsichord, Barchet Quartet, Pro Musica Orch. of Stuttgart, under Reinhardt. Francesco Geminiani (1687-1762) has been rediscovered in the same musical exploration that revealed Scarlatti, Vivaldi, and Corelli. In form he is more sophisticated than the earlier Italians, but his music delights modern listeners with its combination of contrapuntal techniques and the full harmonies and rich melodies charcteristic of Italian music. This is the only recording of the six 1733 concerti: D Major, B Flat Minor, E Minor, G Minor, E Minor (bis), and D Minor. "I warmly recommend it, spacious, magnificent, I enjoyed every bar," C. Cudworth, RECORD NEWS. "Works of real charm, recorded with understanding and style," ETUDE. (Playing time 52 mins.)
                                                                  HCR 5209 $2.00

MODERN PIANO SONATAS: BARTOK: SONATA FOR PIANO; BLOCH: SONATA FOR PIANO (1935); PROKOFIEV, PIANO SONATA #7 IN B FLAT ("STALINGRAD"); STRAVINSKY: PIANO SONATA (1924), István Nádas, Piano. Shows some of the major forces and directions in modern piano music: Stravinsky's crisp austerity; Bartok's fusion of Hungarian folk motives; incisive diverse rhythms, and driving power; Bloch's distinctive emotional vigor; Prokofiev's brilliance and melodic beauty couched in pre-Romantic forms. "A most interesting documentation of the contemporary piano sonata. Nadas is a very good pianist." HIGH FIDELITY. (Playing time 59 mins.)   **HCR 5215 $2.00**

VIVALDI: CONCERTI FOR FLUTE, VIOLIN, BASSOON, AND HARPSICHORD: #8 IN G MINOR, #21 IN F, #27 IN D, #7 IN D; SONATA #1 IN A MINOR, Gastone Tassinari, Renato Giangrandi, Giorgio Semprini, Arlette Eggmann. More than any other Baroque composer, Vivaldi moved the concerto grosso closer to the solo concert we deem standard today. In these concerti he wrote virtuosi music for the solo instruments, allowing each to introduce new material or expand on musical ideas, creating tone colors unusual even for Vivaldi. As a result, this record displays a new area of his genius, offering some of his most brilliant music. Performed by a top-rank European group. (Playing time 45 mins.)   **HCR 5216 $2.00**

LÜBECK: CANTATAS: HILF DEINEM VOLK; GOTT, WIE DEIN NAME, Stuttgart Choral Society, Swabian Symphony Orch.; PRELUDES AND FUGUES IN C MINOR AND IN E, Eva Hölderlin, Organ. Vincent Lübeck (1654-1740), contemporary of Bach and Buxtehude, was one of the great figures of the 18th-century North German school. These examples of Lübeck's few surviving works indicate his power and brilliance. Voice and instrument lines in the cantatas are strongly reminiscent of the organ: the preludes and fugues show the influence of Bach and Buxtehude. This is the only recording of the superb cantatas. Text and translation included. "Outstanding record," E. T. Canby, SAT. REVIEW. "Hölderlin's playing is exceptional," AM. RECORD REVIEW. "Will make [Lübeck] many new friends," Philip Miller. (Playing time 37 mins.)   **HCR 5217 $2.00**

DONIZETTI: BETLY (LA CAPANNA SVIZZERA), Soloists of Compagnia del Teatro dell'Opera Comica di Roma, Societa del Quartetto, Rome, Chorus and Orch. Betly, a delightful one-act opera written in 1836, is similar in style and story to one of Donizetti's better-known operas, L'Elisir. Betly is lighthearted and farcical, with bright melodies and a freshness characteristic of the best of Donizetti. Libretto (English and Italian) included. "The chief honors go to Angela Tuccari who sings the title role, and the record is worth having for her alone," M. Rayment, GRAMOPHONE REC. REVIEW. "The interpretation . . . is excellent . . . This is a charming record which we recommend to lovers of little-known works," DISQUES.
HCR 5218 **$2.00**

ROSSINI: L'OCCASIONE FA IL LADRO (IL CAMBIO DELLA VALIGIA), Soloists of Compagnia del Teatro dell'Opera Comica di Roma, Societa del Quartetto, Rome, Chorus and Orch. A charming one-act opera buffa, this is one of the first works of Rossini's maturity, and it is filled with the wit, gaiety and sparkle that make his comic operas second only to Mozart's. Like other Rossini works, L'Occasione makes use of the theme of impersonation and attendant amusing confusions. This is the only recording of this important buffa. Full libretto (English and Italian) included. "A major rebirth, a stylish performance . . . the Roman recording engineers have outdone themselves," H. Weinstock, SAT. REVIEW. (Playing time 53 mins.)
HCR 5219 **$2.00**

DOWLAND: "FIRST BOOKE OF AYRES," Pro Musica Antiqua of Brussels, Safford Cape, Director. This is the first recording to include all 22 of the songs of this great collection, written by John Dowland, one of the most important writers of songs of 16th and 17th century England. The participation of the Brussels Pro Musica under Safford Cape insures scholarly accuracy and musical artistry. "Powerfully expressive and very beautiful," B. Haggin. "The musicianly singers . . . never fall below an impressive standard," Philip Miller. Text included. (Playing time 51 mins.)
HCR 5220 **$2.00**

FRENCH CHANSONS AND DANCES OF THE 16TH CENTURY, Pro Musica Antiqua of Brussels, Safford Cape, Director. A remarkable selection of 26 three- or four-part chansons and delightful dances from the French Golden Age—by such composers as Orlando Lasso, Crecquillon, Claude Gervaise, etc. Text and translation included. "Delightful, well-varied with respect to mood and to vocal and instrumental color," HIGH FIDELITY. "Performed with . . . discrimination and musical taste, full of melodic distinction and harmonic resource," Irving Kolodin. (Playing time 39 mins.)
HCR 5221 **$2.00**

GALUPPI: CONCERTI A QUATRO: #1 IN G MINOR, #2 IN G, #3 IN D, #4 IN C MINOR, #5 IN E FLAT, AND #6 IN B FLAT, Biffoli Quartet. During Baldassare Galuppi's lifetime, his instrumental music was widely renowned, and his contemporaries Mozart and Haydn thought highly of his work. These 6 concerti reflect his great ability; and they are among the most interesting compositions of the period. They are remarkable for their unusual combinations of timbres and for emotional elements that were only then beginning to be introduced into music. Performed by the well-known Biffoli Quartet, this is the only record devoted exclusively to Galuppi. (Playing time 47 mins.)
HCR 5222 **$2.00**

HAYDN: DIVERTIMENTI FOR WIND BAND, IN C; IN F; DIVERTIMENTO A NOVE STROMENTI IN C FOR STRINGS AND WIND INSTRUMENTS, reconstructed by H. C. Robbins Landon, performed by members of Vienna State Opera Orch.; **MOZART DIVERTIMENTI IN C, III (K. 187) AND IV (K. 188), Salzburg Wind Ensemble.** Robbins Landon discovered Haydn manuscripts in a Benedictine monastery in Lower Austria, edited them and restored their original instrumentation. The result is this magnificent record. Two little-known divertimenti by Mozart—of great charm and appeal—are also included. None of this music is available elsewhere (Playing time 58 mins.)
HCR 5223 **$2.00**

PURCELL: TRIO SONATAS FROM "SONATAS OF FOUR PARTS" (1697): #9 IN F ("GOLDEN"), #7 IN C, #1 IN B MINOR, #10 IN D, #4 IN D MINOR, #2 IN E FLAT, AND #8 IN G MINOR, Giorgio Ciompi, and Werner Torkanowsky, Violins, Geo. Koutzen, Cello, and Herman Chessid, Harpsichord. These posthumously-published sonatas show Purcell at his most advanced and mature. They are certainly among the finest musical examples of pre-modern chamber music. Those not familiar with his instrumental music are well-advised to hear these outstanding pieces. "Performance sounds excellent," Harold Schonberg. "Some of the most noble and touching music known to anyone," AMERICAN RECORD GUIDE. (Playing time 58 mins.)
HCR 5224 **$2.00**

BARTOK: VIOLIN CONCERTO; SONATA FOR UNACCOMPANIED VIOLIN, Ivry Gitlis, Pro Musica of Vienna, under Hornstein. Both these works are outstanding examples of Bartok's final period, and they show his powers at their fullest. The Violin Concerto is, in the opinion of many authorities, Bartok's finest work, and the Sonata, his last work, is "a masterpiece" (F. Sackville West). "Wonderful, finest performance of both Bartok works I have ever heard," GRAMOPHONE. "Gitlis makes such potent and musical sense out of these works that I suspect many general music lovers (not otherwise in sympathy with modern music) will discover to their amazement that they like it. Exceptionally good sound," AUDITOR. (Playing time 54 mins.)
HCR 5211 **$2.00**

J. S. BACH: PARTITAS FOR UNACCOMPANIED VIOLIN: #2 in D Minor and #3 in E, Bronislav Gimpel. Bach's works for unaccompanied violin fall within the same area that produced the Brandenburg Concerti, the Orchestral Suites, and the first part of the Well-Tempered Clavichord. The D Minor is considered one of Bach's masterpieces; the E Major is a buoyant work with exceptionally interesting bariolage effects. This is the first release of a truly memorable recording by Bronislav Gimpel, "as a violinist, the equal of the greatest" (P. Leron, in OPERA, Paris). (Playing time 53 mins.)   HCR 5212 **$2.00**

ROSSINI: QUARTETS FOR WOODWINDS: #1 IN F, #4 IN B FLAT, #5 IN D, AND #6 IN F, N. Y. Woodwind Quartet Members: S. Baron, Flute, J. Barrows, French Horn; B. Garfield, Bassoon; D. Glazer, Clarinet. Rossini's great genius was centered in the opera, but he also wrote a small amount of first-rate non-vocal music. Among these instrumental works, first place is usually given to the very interesting quartets. Of the three different surviving arrangements, this wind group version is the original, and this is the first recording of these works. "Each member of the group displays wonderful virtuosity when the music calls for it, at other times blending sensitively into the ensemble," HIGH FIDELITY. "Sheer delight," Philip Miller. (Playing time 45 mins.)   HCR 5214 **$2.00**

TELEMANN: THE GERMAN FANTASIAS FOR HARPSICHORD (#1-12), Helma Elsner. Until recently, Georg Philip Telemann (1681-1767) was one of the mysteriously neglected great men of music. Recently he has received the attention he deserved. He created music that delights modern listeners with its freshness and originality. These fantasias are free in form and reveal the intricacy of thorough bass music, the harmonic wealth of the "new music," and a distinctive melodic beauty. "This is another blessing of the contemporary LP output. Miss Elsner plays with considerable sensitivity and a great deal of understanding," REV. OF RECORDED MUSIC. "Fine recorded sound," Harold Schonberg. "Recommended warmly, very high quality," DISQUES. (Playing time 50 mins.)   HCR 5210 **$2.00**

Nova Recordings

In addition to our reprints of outstanding out-of-print records and American releases of first-rate foreign recordings, we have established our own new records. In order to keep every phase of their production under our own control, we have engaged musicians of world renown to play important music (for the most part unavailable elsewhere), have made use of the finest recording studios in New York, and have produced tapes equal to anything on the market, we believe. The first of these entirely new records are now available.

RAVEL: GASPARD DE LA NUIT, LE TOMBEAU DE COUPERIN, JEUX D'EAU, Beveridge Webster, Piano. Webster studied under Ravel and played his works in European recitals, often with Ravel's personal participation in the program. This record offers examples of the three major periods of Ravel's pianistic work, and is a must for any serious collector or music lover. (Playing time about 50 minutes).   Monaural HCR 5213 **$2.00**
                                                                                Stereo HCR ST 7000 **$2.00**

EIGHTEENTH CENTURY FRENCH FLUTE MUSIC, Jean-Pierre Rampal, Flute, and Robert Veyron-Lacroix, Harpsichord. Contains Concerts Royaux #7 for Flute and Harpsichord in G Minor, Francois Couperin; Sonata dite l'Inconnue in G for Flute and Harpsichord, Michel de la Barre; Sonata #6 in A Minor, Michel Blavet; and Sonata in D Minor, Anne Danican-Philidor. In the opinion of many Rampal is the world's premier flutist. (Playing time about 45 minutes)
                                                                                Monaural HCR 5238 **$2.00**
                                                                                Stereo HCR ST 7001 **$2.00**

SCHUMANN: NOVELLETTEN (Opus 21), Beveridge Webster, Piano. Brilliantly played in this original recording by one of America's foremost keyboard performers. Connected Romantic pieces. Long a piano favorite. (Playing time about 45 minutes)
                                                                                Monaural HCR 5239 **$2.00**
                                                                                Stereo HCR ST 7002 **$2.00**

Teach Yourself

These British books are the most effective series of home study books on the market! With no outside help they will teach you as much as is necessary to have a good background in each subject, in many cases offering as much material as a similar high school or college course. They are carefully planned, written by foremost British educators, and amply provided with test questions and problems for you to check your progress; the mathematics books are especially rich in examples and problems. Do not confuse them with skimpy outlines or ordinary school texts or vague generalized popularizations; each book is complete in itself, full without being overdetailed, and designed to give you an easily-acquired branch of knowledge.

TEACH YOURSELF ALGEBRA, P. Abbott. The equivalent of a thorough high school course, up through logarithms. 52 illus. 307pp. 4¼ x 7. T680 Clothbound **$2.00**

TEACH YOURSELF GEOMETRY, P. Abbott. Plane and solid geometry, covering about a year of plane and six months of solid. 268 illus. 344pp. 4½ x 7. T681 Clothbound **$2.00**

TEACH YOURSELF TRIGONOMETRY, P. Abbott. Background of algebra and geometry will enable you to get equivalent of elementary college course. Tables. 102 illus. 204pp. 4½ x 7. T682 Clothbound **$2.00**

TEACH YOURSELF THE CALCULUS, P. Abbott. With algebra and trigonometry you will be able to acquire a good working knowledge of elementary integral calculus and differential calculus. Excellent supplement to any course textbook. 380pp. 4¼ x 7. T683 Clothbound **$2.00**

TEACH YOURSELF THE SLIDE RULE, B. Snodgrass. Basic principles clearly explained, with many applications in engineering, business, general figuring, will enable you to pick up very useful skill. 10 illus. 207pp. 4¼ x 7. T684 Clothbound **$2.00**

TEACH YOURSELF MECHANICS, P. Abbott. Equivalent of part course on elementary college level, with lever, parallelogram of force, friction, laws of motion, gases, etc. Fine introduction before more advanced course. 163 illus. 271pp. 4½ x 7. T685 Clothbound **$2.00**

TEACH YOURSELF ELECTRICITY, C. W. Wilman. Current, resistance, voltage, Ohm's law, circuits, generators, motors, transformers, etc. Non-mathematical as much as possible. 115 illus. 184pp. 4¼ x 7. T230 Clothbound **$2.00**

TEACH YOURSELF HEAT ENGINES E. DeVille. Steam and internal combustion engines; nonmathematical introduction for student, for layman wishing background, refresher for advanced student. 76 illus. 217pp. 4¼ x 7. T237 Clothbound **$2.00**

TEACH YOURSELF TO PLAY THE PIANO, King Palmer. Companion and supplement to lessons or self study. Handy reference, too. Nature of instrument, elementary musical theory, technique of playing, interpretation, etc. 60 illus. 144pp. 4¼ x 7. T959 Clothbound **$2.00**

TEACH YOURSELF HERALDRY AND GENEALOGY, L. G. Pine. Modern work, avoiding romantic and overpopular misconceptions. Editor of new Burke presents detailed information and commentary down to present. Best general survey. 50 illus. glossary; 129pp. 4¼ x 7. T962 Clothbound **$2.00**

TEACH YOURSELF HANDWRITING, John L. Dumpleton. Basic Chancery cursive style is popular and easy to learn. Many diagrams. 114 illus. 192pp. 4¼ x 7. T960 Clothbound **$2.00**

TEACH YOURSELF CARD GAMES FOR TWO, Kenneth Konstam. Many first-rate games, including old favorites like cribbage and gin and canasta as well as new lesser-known games. Extremely interesting for cards enthusiast. 60 illus. 150pp. 4¼ x 7. T963 Clothbound **$2.00**

TEACH YOURSELF GUIDEBOOK TO THE DRAMA, Luis Vargas. Clear, rapid survey of changing fashions and forms from Aeschylus to Tennessee Williams, in all major European traditions. Plot summaries, critical comments, etc. Equivalent of a college drama course; fine cultural background 224pp. 4¼ x 7. T961 Clothbound **$2.00**

TEACH YOURSELF THE ORGAN, Francis Routh. Excellent compendium of background material for everyone interested in organ music, whether as listener or player. 27 musical illus. 158pp. 4¼ x 7. T977 Clothbound **$2.00**

TEACH YOURSELF TO STUDY SCULPTURE, William Gaunt. Noted British cultural historian surveys culture from Greeks, primitive world, to moderns. Equivalent of college survey course. 23 figures, 40 photos. 158pp. 4¼ x 7. T976 Clothbound **$2.00**

History, Political Science

THE POLITICAL THOUGHT OF PLATO AND ARISTOTLE, E. Barker. One of the clearest and most accurate expositions of the corpus of Greek political thought. This standard source contains exhaustive analyses of the "Republic" and other Platonic dialogues and Aristotle's "Politics" and "Ethics," and discusses the origin of these ideas in Greece, contributions of other Greek theorists, and modifications of Greek ideas by thinkers from Aquinas to Hegel. "Must" reading for anyone interested in the history of Western thought. Index. Chronological Table of Events. 2 Appendixes. xxiv + 560pp. 5⅜ x 8. T521 Paperbound **$2.50**

THE IDEA OF PROGRESS, J. B. Bury. Practically unknown before the Reformation, the idea of progress has since become one of the central concepts of western civilization. Prof. Bury analyzes its evolution in the thought of Greece, Rome, the Middle Ages, the Renaissance, to its flowering in all branches of science, religion, philosophy, industry, art, and literature, during and following the 16th century. Introduction by Charles Beard. Index. xl + 357pp. 5⅜ x 8. T40 Paperbound **$2.00**

THE ANCIENT GREEK HISTORIANS, J. B. Bury. This well known, easily read work covers the entire field of classical historians from the early writers to Herodotus, Thucydides, Xenophon, through Poseidonius and such Romans as Tacitus, Cato, Caesar, Livy. Scores of writers are studied biographically, in style, sources, accuracy, structure, historical concepts, and influences. Recent discoveries such as the Oxyrhinchus papyri are referred to, as well as such great scholars as Nissen, Gomperz, Cornford, etc. "Totally unblemished by pedantry." Outlook. "The best account in English," Dutcher, A Guide to Historical Lit. Bibliography, Index. x + 281pp. 5⅜ x 8. T397 Paperbound **$1.65**

HISTORY OF THE LATER ROMAN EMPIRE, J. B. Bury. This standard work by the leading Byzantine scholar of our time discusses the later Roman and early Byzantine empires from 395 A.D. through the death of Justinian in 565, in their political, social, cultural, theological, and military aspects. Contemporary documents are quoted in full, making this the most complete reconstruction of the period and a fit successor to Gibbon's "Decline and Fall." "Most unlikely that it will ever be superseded," Glanville Downey, Dumbarton Oaks Research Lib. Geneological tables. 5 maps. Bibliography. Index. 2 volumes total of 965pp. 5⅜ x 8. T398, 399 Two volume set, Paperbound **$4.50**

A HISTORY OF ANCIENT GEOGRAPHY, E. H. Bunbury. Standard study, in English, of ancient geography; never equalled for scope, detail. First full account of history of geography from Greeks' first world picture based on mariners, through Ptolemy. Discusses every important map, discovery, figure, travel expedition, war, conjecture, narrative, bearing on subject. Chapters on Homeric geography, Herodotus, Alexander expedition, Strabo, Pliny, Ptolemy, would stand alone as exhaustive monographs. Includes minor geographers, men not usually regarded in this context: Hecataeus, Pytheas, Hipparchus, Artemidorus, Marinus of Tyre, etc. Uses information gleaned from military campaigns such as Punic Wars, Hannibal's passage of Alps, campaigns of Lucullus, Pompey, Caesar's wars, the Trojan War. New introduction by W. H. Stahl, Brooklyn College. Bibliography. Index. 20 maps. 1426pp. 5⅜ x 8. T570-1, clothbound, 2-volume set **$12.50**

POLITICAL PARTIES, Robert Michels. Classic of social science, reference point for all later work, deals with nature of leadership in social organization on government and trade union levels. Probing tendency of oligarchy to replace democracy, it studies need for leadership, desire for organization, psychological motivations, vested interests, hero worship, reaction of leaders to power, press relations, many other aspects. Trans. by E. & C. Paul. Introduction. 447pp. 5⅜ x 8. T569 Paperbound **$2.00**

A HISTORY OF HISTORICAL WRITING, Harry Elmer Barnes. Virtually the only adequate survey of the whole course of historical writing in a single volume. Surveys developments from the beginnings of historiographies in the ancient Near East and the Classical World, up through the Cold War. Covers major historians in detail, shows interrelationship with cultural background, makes clear individual contributions, evaluates and estimates importance; also enormously rich upon minor authors and thinkers who are usually passed over. Packed with scholarship and learning, clear, easily written. Indispensable to every student of history. Revised and enlarged up to 1961. Index and bibliography. xv + 442pp. 5⅜ x 8½. T104 Paperbound **$2.25**

Prices subject to change without notice.

Dover publishes books on art, music, philosophy, literature, languages, history, social sciences, psychology, handcrafts, orientalia, puzzles and entertainments, chess, pets and gardens, books explaining science, intermediate and higher mathematics, mathematical physics, engineering, biological sciences, earth sciences, classics of science, etc. Write to:

Dept. catrr.
Dover Publications, Inc.
180 Varick Street, N. Y. 14, N. Y.